9780895794246

Die drei Pintos

RECENT RESEARCHES IN MUSIC

A-R Editions publishes seven series of critical editions, spanning the history of Western music, American music, and oral traditions.

RECENT RESEARCHES IN THE MUSIC OF THE MIDDLE AGES AND EARLY RENAISSANCE
    Charles M. Atkinson, general editor

RECENT RESEARCHES IN THE MUSIC OF THE RENAISSANCE
    James Haar, general editor

RECENT RESEARCHES IN THE MUSIC OF THE BAROQUE ERA
    Christoph Wolff, general editor

RECENT RESEARCHES IN THE MUSIC OF THE CLASSICAL ERA
    Eugene K. Wolf, general editor

RECENT RESEARCHES IN THE MUSIC OF THE NINETEENTH AND EARLY TWENTIETH CENTURIES
    Rufus Hallmark, general editor

RECENT RESEARCHES IN AMERICAN MUSIC
    John M. Graziano, general editor

RECENT RESEARCHES IN THE ORAL TRADITIONS OF MUSIC
    Philip V. Bohlman, general editor

Each edition in *Recent Researches* is devoted to works by a single composer or to a single genre. The content is chosen for its high quality and historical importance, and each edition includes a substantial introduction and critical report. The music is engraved according to the highest standards of production using the proprietary software MUSE, owned by MusicNotes, Inc.

For information on establishing a standing order to any of our series, or for editorial guidelines on submitting proposals, please contact:

A-R Editions, Inc.
801 Deming Way
Madison, Wisconsin 53717

800 736-0070 (U.S. book orders)
608 836-9000 (phone)
608 831-8200 (fax)
http://www.areditions.com

RECENT RESEARCHES IN THE MUSIC OF THE NINETEENTH AND EARLY TWENTIETH CENTURIES, 31

Gustav Mahler

Die drei Pintos

Based on Sketches and Original Music of
Carl Maria von Weber

Part II:

Act 2, Act 3, Critical Report

Edited by James L. Zychowicz

Libretto Translated by
Charlotte Brancaforte and Salvatore Calomino

A-R Editions, Inc.
Madison

A-R Editions, Inc., Madison, Wisconsin 53717
© 2000 by A-R Editions, Inc.

All rights reserved. No part of this book may be reproduced or transmitted in any form by any electronic or mechanical means (including photocopying, recording, or information storage and retrieval) without permission in writing from the publisher.

The purchase of this edition does not convey the right to perform it in public, nor to make a recording of it for any purpose. Such permission must be obtained in advance from the publisher.

A-R Editions is pleased to support scholars and performers in their use of *Recent Researches* material for study or performance. Subscribers to any of the *Recent Researches* series, as well as patrons of subscribing institutions, are invited to apply for information about our "Copyright Sharing Policy."

Printed in the United States of America

ISBN 0-89579-424-1
ISSN 0193-5364

♾ The paper used in this publication meets the minimum requirements of the American National Standard for Information Sciences—Permanence of Paper for Printed Library Materials, ANSI Z39.48-1984.

Contents

Part I

Acknowledgments   vii

Introduction   ix

   Weber and *Die drei Pintos*   ix
   Die drei Pintos after Weber's Death   x
   Mahler and *Die drei Pintos*   xi
   The Completion and Premiere of *Die drei Pintos*   xv
   Die drei Pintos and the Problem of Authorship   xvi
   Performance Considerations   xvii
   Notes   xviii

Libretto and Translation   xxi

   Personen / Characters   xxi
   Ort der Handlung / Scene of the Action   xxii
   Erster Aufzug / Act One   xxii
   Zweiter Aufzug / Act Two   xliii
   Dritter Aufzug / Act Three   lii

Plates   lxxiv

Die drei Pintos

I. Aufzug   3

   No. 1. Ensemble (Gaston, Ambrosio, Chorus): "Leeret die Becher"   3
   No. 2. Rondo a la Polacca (Gaston): "Was ich dann thu'"   47
   No. 3. Terzettino (Gaston, Ambrosio, Der Wirth): "Ei, wer hätte das gedacht!"   59
   No. 4. Romanze von dem verliebten Kater Mansor (Inez): "Leise weht' es"   63
   No. 5. Seguidilla a dos (Inez, Gaston): "Wir, die den Musen dienen"   68
   No. 6. Terzett (Gaston, Ambrosio, Pinto): "Also frisch das Werk begonnen"   85
   No. 7. Finale (Inez, Gaston, Ambrosio, Pinto, Chorus): "Auf das Wohlergeh'n der Gäste!"   134

Entr'act   206

Part II

II. Aufzug   237

   No. 8. Introduction und Ensemble (Clarissa, Laura, Pantaleone, Chorus): "Wißt Ihr nicht, was wir hier sollen?"   237
   No. 9. Ariette (Laura): "'Höchste Lust'"   301
   No. 10. Rezitativ und Arie (Clarissa): "Ach, wenn das Du doch vermöchtest" / "Wonne, süßes Hoffnungsträumen"   305
   No. 11. Duett (Clarissa, Gomez): "Ja, das Wort"   321
   No. 12. Terzett-Finale (Clarissa, Laura, Gomez): "Geschwind nur von hinnen"   336

III. Aufzug 359

   No. 13. Lied mit Chor (Laura, Chorus): "Schmücket die Halle" 359
   No. 14. Duett (Gaston, Ambrosio): "Nun da sind wir" 378
   No. 15. Terzettino (Laura, Gaston, Ambrosio): "Mädchen, ich leide heiße
       Liebespein" 398
   No. 16. Ariette (Ambrosio): "Ein Mädchen verloren" 403
   No. 17. Rondo-Terzett (Gomez, Gaston, Ambrosio): "Ihr, der so edel" 411
   No. 18. Chor (Chorus): "Habt Ihr es denn schon vernommen?" 434
   No. 19. Mädchenlied (Chorus): "Mit lieblichen Blumen" 451
   No. 20. Finale A (Clarissa, Laura, Gomez, Gaston, Ambrosio, Pantaleone,
       Pinto, Chorus): "Was wollt Ihr?" 460
   No. 21. Finale B (Clarissa, Laura, Gomez, Gaston, Ambrosio, Pantaleone, Chorus):
       "Heil sei Euch" 530

Critical Report 561

   Sources 561
   Editorial Methods 561
   Critical Notes 563
   Mahler's Revisions for the Kahnt Score 567
   Text Cues in the Kahnt Score 569
   Notes 570

II. Aufzug
No. 8. Introduction und Ensemble

*Für den Fall des Sprungs erhält die erste Violins statt des f zwischen der ersten und zweiten Linie: $\frac{1}{4}$ [ein Viertel] f in der Octave. Viol. 2, Viola, Cello, und Bass erhalten eine Viertelspause zu.

264

265

153
Fl. 1, 2
Ob. 1, 2
Cl. 1, 2
Bn. 1, 2
Hn. 1, 2
Hn. 3, 4
Tpt. 1, 2
Trb. 1, 2
Trb. 3
Tb.
Timp.
Vn. 1
Vn. 2
Va.
S
A
T
B
Vc.
Cb.
molto rit.
a 2
[in D-A]
arco
schon!

267

164
Vn. 1
Vn. 2
Va.
Pant.
Vc.
Cb.
tr
f
p
Be- ru- fen hab' ich Dich hier-her, mein
169
Kind, und Euch als __ Zeu- gen, lie- be Viel- ge- treu- e, daß Ihr ver- nehmt, was
174
Tpt. 1, 2
pp
wir ge- son- nen sind zu thun, und Je- der __ sich da- rob er- freu- e!

179
Bewegter
Fl. 1, 2
Ob. 1, 2
Cl. 1, 2
Bn. 1, 2
Hn. 1, 2
Bewegter
Springbogen
arco
pizz.
Vn. 1
Vn. 2
Va.
Pant.
S
Wir sind da- zu be- reit,
A
Wir sind da- zu be- reit,
T
Wir sind da- zu be- reit,
B
Wir sind da- zu be- reit,
Vc.
Cb.

vi-
183
H
Einlenkend zum Tempo
divisi
Vn. 1
Vn. 2
Va.
Pant.
Don Ru- iz de Pa- che- co al- tem
S
im Vor- aus schon er- freut!
A
im Vor- aus schon er- freut!
T
im Vor- aus schon er- freut!
B
im Vor- aus schon er- freut!
[arco]
Vc.
Cb.
Tempo I
187
Fl. 1
Picc.
Ob. 1, 2
Tempo I
Vn. 1
Vn. 2
divisi
Va.
Pant.
Stam- me ent- sproßt nur ei- ne einz'- ge Blü- the noch:
Vc.
Cb.

271

202
J
Fl. 1, 2
Ob. 1, 2
Cl. 1, 2
Bn. 1, 2
Hn. 1, 2
Vn. 1
Vn. 2
Va.
Pant.
S
A
T
B
Vc.
Cb.
a 2
pp
cresc.
[cresc.]
D'rum hab' ich Dir 'nen Bräu- ti- gam er-
doch sprecht nur wei- ter, sprecht!
(Im Vor- aus schon er- freut!)

rit.
206
Fl. 1, 2
Ob. 1, 2
Cl. 1, 2
Bn. 1, 2
Hn. 1, 2
rit.
Vn. 1
Vn. 2
Va.
Pant.
-le- sen, mein Kind, Cla- ris- sa, Du bist Braut, ja,
Vc.
Cb.
arco
mf
p
Tempo I
209
vi-
tr
11
6
ja, Cla- (Don) ris- sa, Du bist Braut, Cla- ris- sa, Du bist Braut, und

274

ein Fon- se- ca, des- sen Va- ter einst ge- we- sen ein Ret- ter mir, Don Pin- to, wird Dir

an- ge- traut, ja an- ge- traut, Don Pin- to wird Dir an- ge- traut!

223
Bewegter
Fl. 1, 2
a 2
p
Ob. 1, 2
a 2
p
Cl. 1, 2
a 2
p
Bn. 1, 2
p
Hn. 1, 2
pp
Hn. 3, 4
pp
Tpt. 1, 2
[1]
p
Trb. 1, 2
1
p
Bewegter
Vn. 1
pp
Vn. 2
Va.
Clar.
Don Pin- to, Va- ter, nein!
Laura
Da schlägt der Blitz schon ein!
S
pp
Das nenn' ich Va- ter
A
pp
Das nenn' ich Va- ter
T
pp
Das nenn' ich Va- ter
B
pp
Das nenn' ich Va- ter
Vc.
Cb.

226
K
Fl. 1, 2
Ob. 1, 2
Cl. 1, 2
Bn. 1, 2
a 2
Hn. 1, 2
Hn. 3, 4
Tpt. 1, 2
Trb. 1, 2
[1]
1
cresc.
[cresc.]
Vn. 1
Vn. 2
Va.
Pant.
Und
S
A
T
B
sein, welch' glück- li- cher Ver- ein, das nenn' ich Va- ter sein, welch' glück- li- cher Ver- ein!
Vc.
Cb.
tr
f
fp
mf

230
rit.
Vn. 1
Vn. 2
Va.
Pant.
Vc.
Cb.
cresc.
[cresc.]
heu- te schon, so zeigt des Brie- fes Da- tum, trifft er hier- ein und for- dert Dei- ne
236
Etwas breiter
Fl. 1, 2
Ob. 1, 2
Cl. 1, 2
Hn. 1, 2
Hn. 3, 4
Hand. D'rum preist mit mir das wun- der- ba- re

278

Allegro
Lebhaft bewegt, doch nicht überhetzt
243
Ob. 1, 2
a 2
ff
Cl. 1, 2
a 2
ff
Allegro
Lebhaft bewegt, doch nicht überhetzt
S
Wel-che Won- ne, welch' Ent- zü- cken, wel-che Won- ne, welch' Ent-
A
Wel-che Won- ne, welch' Ent- zü- cken, wel-che Won- ne, welch' Ent-
T
Wel-che Won- ne, welch' Ent- zü- cken, wel-che Won- ne, welch' Ent-
B
Wel-che Won- ne, welch' Ent- zü- cken, wel-che Won- ne, welch' Ent-
248
Fl. 1, 2
pp
Ob. 1, 2
pp
Cl. 1, 2
pp
Bn. 1, 2
pp
Hn. 1, 2
pp
Springbogen
Vn. 1
pp
Vn. 2
S
-zü- cken!
A
-zü- cken!
T
-zü- cken!
B
-zü- cken!

Ja, ____ bald strahlt aus Ihren Blicken der Ver-

281

282

L
265
Ob. 1, 2
Cl. 1, 2
Bn. 1, 2
Hn. 1, 2
Clar.
S
A
T
B
a 2
Gott, auf wel- che
ho- her Herr, wir wün- schen Se- gen!
270
Vn. 1
Vn. 2
Va.
Vc.
Cb.
divisi
[arco]
Schick- sals- tü- cken muß ich in die
Hol- de Braut, Dir winkt ent-

274
M
Fl. 1, 2
p espress.
Ob. 1, 2
p espress.
Cl. 1, 2
pp
Bn. 1, 2
pp
Hn. 1, 2
pp
Vn. 1
tr
pp
Vn. 2
pp
Va.
pizz.
pp
Clar.
(hervortretend)
Zu- kunft bli- cken! Wie
Laura
Wie be-
S
pp
-ge- gen schon der Quell der
A
pp
-ge- gen schon der Quell der
T
pp
-ge- gen schon der Quell der
B
pp
-ge- gen schon der Quell der
Vc.
Cb.
pizz.
pp

278
Fl. 1, 2
Ob. 1, 2
Cl. 1, 2
Bn. 1, 2
Hn. 1, 2
(tr)
Vn. 1
Vn. 2
(breit betont)
Va.
Clar.
be- klom- men ist mein Herz, wie
Laura
-klom- men ist das ar- me, ar- me Herz, wie be-
S
rein- sten Lust, hol- de Braut, Dir winkt ent- ge- gen schon der
A
rein- sten Lust, hol- de Braut, Dir winkt ent- ge- gen schon der
T
rein- sten Lust, hol- de
B
rein- sten Lust, ja der Quell der rein- sten Lust, hol- de
Vc.
Cb.

N
282
Fl. 1, 2
Ob. 1, 2
Cl. 1, 2
Bn. 1, 2
Hn. 1, 2
Vn. 1
Vn. 2
Va.
[arco]
Clar.
be- klom- men ist mei- ne Brust! Soll den
Laura
-klom- men ist das Herz, wie be- klom- men ist das Herz! Soll den
Pant.
Jetzt ent- fernt Euch, zu- zu-
S
Quell der rein- sten Lust, der Quell der rein- sten Lust!
A
Quell der rein- sten Lust, der Quell der rein- sten Lust!
T
Braut, Dir winkt ent- ge- gen schon der Quell der Lust!
B
Braut, Dir winkt ent- ge- gen schon der Quell der Lust!
Vc.
arco
Cb.

287
Vn. 1
Vn. 2
divisi
Va.
Clar.
Va- ter ich be- we- gen, wird in ihm sich
Laura
Va- ter sie be- we- gen, wird in ihm sich
Pant.
-schi- cken, was das Fest ver- mag zu schmü- cken, fort, hin- weg ohn' Zeit- ver- lust! Al- les
Vc.
Cb.
292
Vn. 1
Vn. 2
Va.
Clar.
Mit- leid re- gen, daß nicht ster- be je- de
Laura
Mit- leid re- gen, wird in ihm sich Mit- leid re- gen, daß nicht ster- be
Pant.
weg ohn' Zeit- ver- lust, al- les soll die Hän- de re- gen, doch auch dann sich weid- lich
Vc.
Cb.

297
Ob. 1, 2
Vn. 1
Vn. 2
pizz.
Va.
pizz.
Clar.
Lust, daß nicht ster- be je- de
Laura
je- de Lust, daß nicht ster- be je- de Lust!
Pant.
pfle- gen, al- les fort, das Fest zu schmü- cken, al- les fort, ohn' Zeit- ver- lust, ohn' Zeit- ver-
S
Wel-che
A
Wel-che
T
Wel-che
B
Wel-che
Vc.
Cb.

302
O
Fl. 1, 2
a 2
p
Ob. 1, 2
pp
Cl. 1, 2
pp
Bn. 1, 2
pp
Hn. 1, 2
pp
Tpt. 1, 2
1
p
Vn. 1
pp
Vn. 2
Va.
Clar.
Lust!
Pant.
-lust!
S
Won- ne, welch' Ent- zü- cken, wel-che Won- ne, welch' Ent- zü- cken,
A
Won- ne, welch' Ent- zü- cken, wel-che Won- ne, welch' Ent- zü- cken,
T
Won- ne, welch' Ent- zü- cken, wel-che Won- ne, welch' Ent- zü- cken, wel- che
B
Won- ne, welch' Ent- zü- cken, wel-che Won- ne, welch' Ent- zü- cken, wel- che
Vc.
pizz.
pp
Cb.
pp

307
a 2
Fl. 1, 2
Ob. 1, 2
a 2
Cl. 1, 2
Bn. 1, 2
Hn. 1, 2
Tpt. 1, 2
1
Vn. 1
Vn. 2
[arco]
pp
Va.
Pant.
Jetzt _ ent- fernt _ Euch, zu- zu-
S
welch' Ent- zü- cken, wel- che Won- ne, welch' Ent-
A
welch' Ent- zü- cken, wel- che Won- ne, welch' Ent-
T
Won- ne, welch' Ent- zü- cken, welch' Ent-
B
Won- ne, welch' Ent- zü- cken, welch' Ent-
Vc.
arco
ff
Cb.

311
poco accel.
Fl. 1, 2
Ob. 1, 2
Cl. 1, 2
Bn. 1, 2
Hn. 1, 2
Tpt. 1, 2
Trb. 3
Tb.
poco accel.
Vn. 1
Vn. 2
[arco]
Va.
Pant.
-schi- cken, was das Fest ver- mag zu schmü- cken, al- les soll die Hän- de
S
-zü- cken, wel- che Won- ne, wel- che Lust, ho- her Herr, wir wün- schen
A
-zü- cken, wel- che Won- ne, wel- che Lust, ho- her Herr, wir wün- schen
T
-zü- cken, wel- che Won- ne, wel- che Lust, ho- her Herr, wir wün- schen
B
-zü- cken, wel- che Won- ne, wel- che Lust, ho- her Herr, wir wün- schen
Vc.
arco
Cb.

re- gen, doch auch dann sich weid- lich pfle- gen, al- le fort!

Se- gen, schö- ne Braut, Euch strömt ent- ge- gen sel'- ge Lust!

Laß

319
Fl. 1, 2
Ob. 1, 2
Cl. 1, 2
Bn. 1, 2
Hn. 1, 2
Tpt. 1, 2
Trb. 1, 2
Trb. 3
Tb.
Timp.
Vn. 1
Vn. 2
Va.
Clar.
den Va- ter mich be- we- gen, daß nicht
Laura
O laß sie ihn be- we- gen, daß nicht
Pant.
Al- les soll die Hän- de
S
Ho- he Braut, wir wün- schen Se- gen, ho- her Herr, wir wün- schen
A
Ho- he Braut, wir wün- schen Se- gen, ho- her Herr, wir wün- schen
T
Ho- her Herr, wir wün- schen
B
Ho- her Herr, wir wün- schen
Vc.
Cb.
pizz.
arco
[arco]

324
Fl. 1, 2
Ob. 1, 2
1
Cl. 1, 2
Bn. 1, 2
Hn. 1, 2
Tpt. 1, 2
a 2
f
Trb. 1, 2
Trb. 3
Tb.
f
Timp.
f
Vn. 1
Vn. 2
Va.
Clar.
espress.
ster- be je- de Lust, daß
Laura
ster- be je- de Lust,
Pant.
re- gen, al- le fort ohn' Zeit- ver- lust.
S
cresc.
fff
Se- gen, schö- ne Braut, Euch strömt ent- ge- gen sel'- ge Lust,
A
cresc.
fff
Se- gen, schö- ne Braut, Euch strömt ent- ge- gen sel'- ge Lust,
T
[cresc.]
fff
Se- gen, schö- ne Braut, Euch strömt ent- ge- gen sel'- ge Lust,
B
cresc.
fff
Se- gen, schö- ne Braut, Euch strömt ent- ge- gen sel'- ge Lust,
Vc.
Cb.

*Im Falle des Sprungs singen Clarissa und Laura im 2. Takt [m. 329] statt "sterbe": "sterbe jede".

296

*Im Falle des Sprungs erhält Viol. 1 statt $\frac{1}{8}$ [ein Achtel] f: Pause. Viol. 2, Viola, Laura $\frac{1}{4}$ [ein Viertel] f wie Clarissa und die Silbe: "Lust".

341
Fl. 1, 2
Ob. 1, 2
1
Cl. 1, 2
[1]
Bn. 1, 2
Hn. 1, 2
pp
Hn. 3, 4
pp
Vn. 1
p
Vn. 2
arco
pizz.
arco
p
Va.
arco
pizz.
arco
p
Clar.
Lust, daß nicht ster- be je- de Lust, daß nicht ster- be, ster-
Laura
Lust, daß nicht ster- be je- de Lust, daß nicht ster- be, ster- be,
S
Braut, Dir strömt ent- ge- gen schon der Quell der rein- sten
A
Braut, Dir strömt ent- ge- gen schon der Quell der rein- sten
T
Braut, Dir strömt ent- ge- gen schon der Quell der rein- sten
B
Braut, Dir strömt ent- ge- gen schon der Quell der rein- sten
Vc. Cb.
arco
pizz.
arco
p

347
a 2
Schnell
Fl. 1, 2
Ob. 1, 2
Cl. 1, 2
Bn. 1, 2
Hn. 1, 2
cresc.
Hn. 3, 4
cresc.
Trb. 3
Tb.
pp [cresc.]
Schnell
Vn. 1
Vn. 2
Va.
Clar.
- - - be je- de Lust!
Laura
ster- - - be je- de Lust!
S
Lust, der Quell der rein- sten Lust!
A
Lust, der Quell der rein- sten Lust!
T
Lust, der Quell der rein- sten Lust!
B
Lust, der Quell der rein- sten Lust!
Vc.
Cb.

353
Fl. 1, 2
Ob. 1, 2
Cl. 1, 2
Bn. 1, 2
Hn. 1, 2
Hn. 3, 4
Trb. 3
Tb.
Timp.
Vn. 1
Vn. 2
Va.
Clar.
Laura
S
A
T
B
Vc.
Cb.
f

No. 9. Ariette

1. "Höch-ste Lust ist treu-es Lie- ben,"
2. "Rein-stes Glück ist treu-es Lie- ben,"

ruft es rings mit tau-send Stim- men, in den Ster- nen siehst Du's flim- men,
lä- chelt Dir's im Mor-gen- strah- le, blinkt Dir's aus der vol- len Scha- le,

302

17
rit.
(sehr kurzer Halt)
Fl. 1, 2
[1]
Ob. 1, 2
Cl. 1, 2
Bn. 1, 2
Hn. 1, 2
rit.
(sehr kurzer Halt)
Vn. 1
divisi
pizz.
Vn. 2
pizz.
arco
Va.
Laura
-schrie- ben, "Höch- ste Lust ist treu- es _ Lie- ben," ja, dort steht's ge-schrie- ben!
Trie- ben, "Rein- stes Glück ist treu- es _ Lie- ben," rein- stes Glück ist Lie- ben!
pizz.
arco
Vc.
arco
pizz.
Cb.
21
Tempo di Valse
[1]
Cl. 1, 2
[1]
Bn. 1, 2
Tempo di Valse
Vn. 1
Vn. 2
pizz.
Va.
Laura
D'rum, Ge- bie- te- rin, _ weg den _ trü- ben _ Sinn, Sor- gen _ weg, Thrä- nen _ weg,
pizz.
Vc.
Cb.

27
[1]
Fl. 1, 2
p
Bn. 1, 2
[1]
Vn. 1
Vn. 2
Va.
Laura
bald lacht das _ höch- ste _ Glück, froh vol- len- det _ sich's, fröh- lich _ en- det _ sich's,
Vc.
Cb.
33
Fl. 1, 2
mf
a 2
f
Ob. 1, 2
[1]
p
a 2
f
Cl. 1, 2
[1]
f
Bn. 1, 2
a 2
mf
f
Hn. 1, 2
f
Trgl.
f
divisi
Vn. 1
mf
f
Vn. 2
divisi
arco
f
Va.
divisi
arco
f
Laura
bald kehrt das Glück wie-der zu-rück in Eu- er Herz!
Vc.
Cb.
f

No. 10. Rezitativ und Arie

306

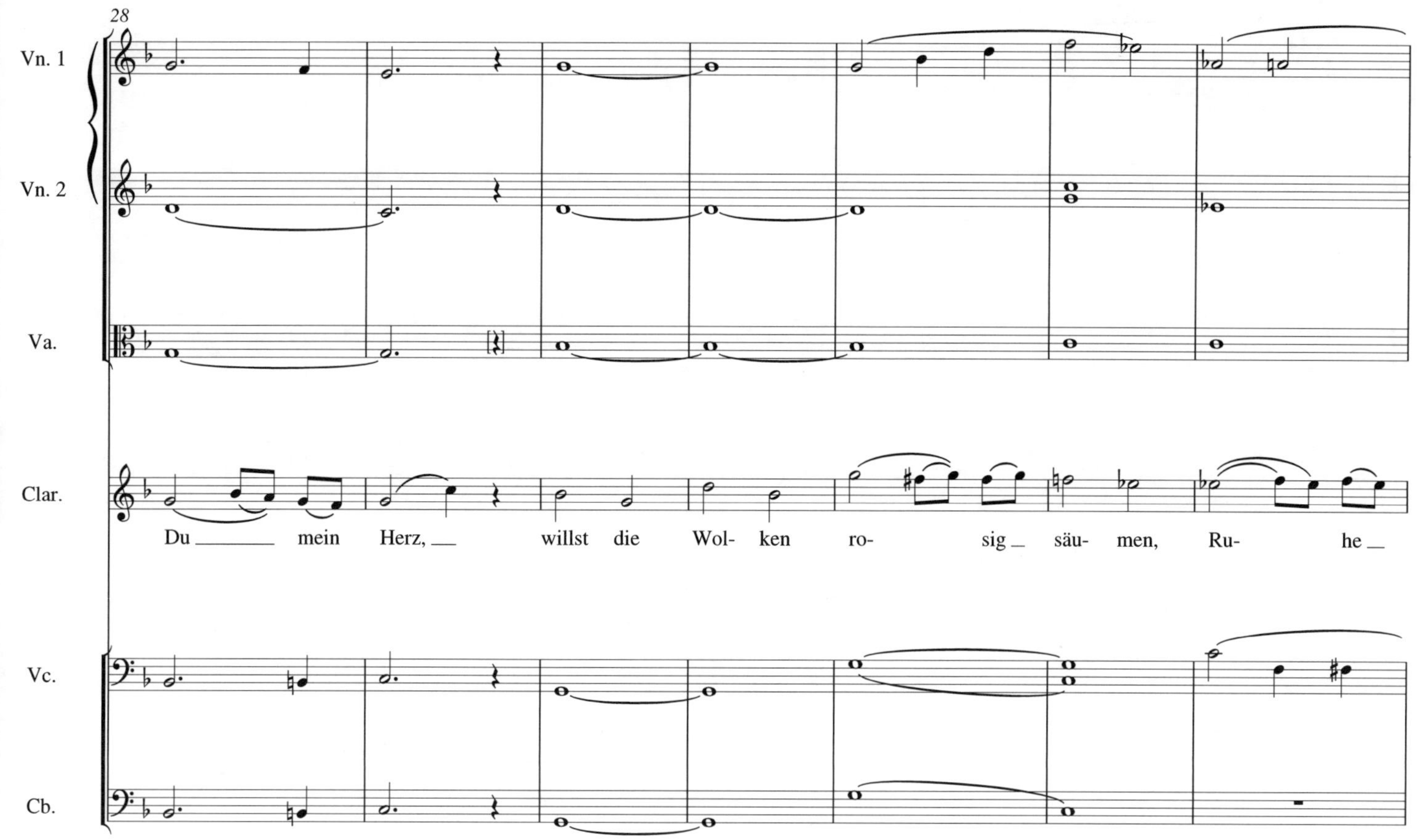
28
Vn. 1
Vn. 2
Va.
Clar.
Du mein Herz, willst die Wol- ken ro- sig säu- men, Ru- he
Vc.
Cb.

B
Nicht schleppen
35
Fl. 1, 2
[1]
pp
Ob. 1, 2
[1]
p espress.
Nicht schleppen
divisi
Vn. 1
ppp
Vn. 2
ppp
Va.
ppp
Clar.
ge- ben mei- nem Schmerz, Ru- he mei- nem Schmerz!
Vc.
ppp

42
[1]
Ob. 1, 2
[1]
Cl. 1, 2
p
Vn. 1
Vn. 2
divisi
Va.
Clar.
Se- lig möcht' ich wei- ter _ träu- men, Schwel- gen
Vc.
Cb.
ppp
49
Vn. 1
pochettino cresc.
Vn. 2
Va.
Clar.
in _ der _ hol- den Lust, _ die nur blüht in Dei- nen Schäu- men;
Vc.
Cb.

309

71
rit.
Hn. 1, 2
Vn. 1
Vn. 2
Va.
Clar.
Vc.
Cb.
77
Mässig beginnend, später allmählig belebt
Fl. 1, 2
pp
gedämpft
Hn. 1, 2
[gedämpft]
Hn. 3, 4
con sordini
pizz.
Ach, wie so ban- ge _ ist Dein Klop-fen, auf die Wan-ge rin-nen Trop-fen

311

92
D
Bn. 1, 2
Vn. 1
senza sordini
Vn. 2
senza sordini
Va.
Clar.
mf espress.
Nie ver- stand ich, nie emp- fand ich,
Vc.
Cb.
96
Bn. 1, 2
Vn. 1
Vn. 2
Va.
Clar.
solch' Ent- zü- cken, sol- che Schmer- zen,
Vc.
Cb.

100
E
Ganz wenig drängend
Ob. 1, 2
Cl. 1, 2
Ganz wenig drängend
Vn. 1
Vn. 2
[arco]
Va.
Clar.
tief im Her- zen! Ein solch' Be- glü- cken
arco
Vc.
Cb.
104
Ob. 1, 2
Cl. 1, 2
Vn. 1
Vn. 2
Va.
Clar.
und Be- drü-cken, als ich in der Lie- be fand, ich in der Lie- be nur emp- fand,
pizz.
arco
Vc.
Cb.

314

315

124
G
divisi
Vn. 1
Vn. 2
arco
Va.
arco
Clar.
wol- le: Eins nur weiß ich fest zu hal- ten,
Vc.
pizz.
Cb.
pizz.
129
Hn. 1, 2
Vn. 1
Vn. 2
Va.
Clar.
wie sich Al- les mag ge- stal- ten,
Vc.
Cb.

133
Ein wenig anhaltend
rit.
Ob. 1, 2
Bn. 1, 2
Hn. 1, 2
Ein wenig anhaltend
rit.
Vn. 1
Vn. 2
col canto
Va.
Clar.
— den Ge- lieb- ten laß ich nicht, den Ge-
arco
Vc.
Cb.
138
a tempo
Ob. 1, 2
Cl. 1, 2
Bn. 1, 2
a tempo
Vn. 1
pizz.
arco
pizz.
Vn. 2
pizz.
arco
pizz.
Va.
Clar.
-lieb- ten laß ich nicht! Wie sich Al- les mag ge- stal- ten, eins nur weiß ich fest zu
pizz.
Vc.
Cb.

318

*Die eingeklammerten kleine Noten gelten für die Sprung.

319

nicht, den Ge- lieb- ten laß ich nicht, den Ge- lieb- ten, den Ge-

-lieb- ten laß ich nicht!

No. 11. Duett

322

10
a tempo
[1]
Ob. 1, 2
p
espress.
Cl. 1, 2
1
pp
Bn. 1, 2
1
pp
Hn. 1, 2
pp
a tempo
Vn. 1
p
Vn. 2
p
Va.
p
Clar.
Lie- be weh- ren soll?
Gom.
Rie- sen- kräf- te schafft die Lie- be, wenn Ihr Ge- gen-lie- be lacht, in das
Vc.
Cb.
13
poco rit.
Ob. 1, 2
Bn. 1, 2
Hn. 1, 2
poco rit.
Vn. 1
pp
Vn. 2
Va.
Gom.
ir- di- sche Ge- trie- be greift sie ein mit Him- mels- macht, greift sie
Vc.
Cb.

B
15
a tempo
Ein wenig drängend
Fl. 1, 2
Ob. 1, 2
Cl. 1, 2
Bn. 1, 2
a tempo
Ein wenig drängend
Vn. 1
Vn. 2
Va.
Clar.
nicht eilen
Darf ich bau- en auf die
Gom.
ein mit _ Him- mels- macht.
Vc.
arco
Cb.
17
Ob. 1, 2
Cl. 1, 2
Bn. 1, 2
pochettino rit.
Vn. 1
Vn. 2
Va.
Clar.
Lie- be, die- sen Stern, der trö- sten wacht, der, ob Al- les dun- kel blie- be, doch den Him- mel hei- ter __
Vc.
arco
Cb.

19
poco accel.
poco rit.
a tempo
Ob. 1, 2
Cl. 1, 2
pp
Bn. 1, 2
pp
poco accel.
poco rit.
a tempo
Vn. 1
poco cresc.
pp
Vn. 2
pp
Va.
pp
(kurzer Halt)
Clar.
macht,
glänzt er im- mer?
Gom.
f
Ja, ver- trau' ihm,
nie-mals un- ter geht sein
Vc.
pp
21
Ob. 1, 2
1
Bn. 1, 2
1
Vn. 1
Vn. 2
Va.
Gom.
Schim-mer, laß uns fol- gen sei- nem Licht, sei das Dun-kel noch so dicht, sei das Dun- kel noch so
Vc.
Cb.
pp

23
Vorwärts
rit. [1]
espress.
Fl. 1, 2
Ob. 1, 2
Cl. 1, 2
Bn. 1, 2
poco cresc.
Hn. 1, 2
poco [cresc.]
Vorwärts
solo
rit.
espress.
[tutti]
Vn. 1
Vn. 2
divisi
Va.
Clar.
Doch Ge-fah-ren! Dei- nem Her-zen un- ter Schmer-zen!
Gom.
dicht! Laß sie dro-hen, trau-e mir nur! He-ge Hoff-nung!
Vc.
Cb.

Grazioso. Poco più mosso
Vn. 1
Vn. 2
Va.
Clar.
Vc.
Cb.
pp
pizz.
arco
So wie
[1]
tr
Cl. 1, 2
Gom.
[pizz.]
p
Blu- men
sprie-ßen, trotz der Stür- me Wü- then, wächst aus
So wie Blü- ten sprie-ßen, trotz der Stür- me Wü- then, wächst aus

C
Ob. 1, 2
Cl. 1, 2
Hn. 1, 2
Vn. 1
Vn. 2
Va.
Clar.
die- ser Stun- den Grau'n: Lie- ben, Hof- fen,
Gom.
die- ser Stun- den Grau'n: Lie- ben, Hof- fen,
Vc. Cb.
Ob. 1, 2
Hn. 1, 2
Vn. 1
Vn. 2
pizz.
Va.
pizz.
Clar.
Lie- ben, Hof- fen, und Ver- trau'n, Lie- ben,
Gom.
Lie- ben, Hof- fen, und Ver- trau'n, Lie- ben,
Vc. Cb.
pizz.

329

45
[1]
Fl. 1, 2
[1]
Ob. 1, 2
p
[1]
Cl. 1, 2
pp
ppp
[1]
Bn. 1, 2
Hn. 1, 2
Vn. 1
ppp
p
pp
Vn. 2
p
pp
Va.
Clar.
Lie- ben, Hof- fen, und Ver- trau'n! So wie
Gom.
Lie- ben, Hof- fen, und Ver- trau'n!
arco
Vc.
Cb.

D
49
Cl. 1, 2
tr
ppp
pp
solo
Vn. 1
ppp
pizz.
Vn. 2
arco
pp
Va.
pizz.
arco
Clar.
Blu- men wol-len in der Stür- me
Gom.
So wie Blü- ten wol-len in der Stür- me
pizz.
Vc.
Cb.
52
[1]
Fl. 1, 2
p
Cl. 1, 2
1
Hn. 1, 2
p
tutti
Vn. 1
ppp
Vn. 2
Va.
Clar.
Wü- then wir nur schö- ne Ta- ge schau'n,
Gom.
Wü- then wir nur schö- ne Ta- ge schau'n,
Vc.

55
Ob. 1, 2
Cl. 1, 2
Bn. 1, 2
Vn. 1
Vn. 2
Va.
Clar.
Gom.
Vc.
Cb.
poco rit.
[1]
solo
pizz.
tutti
arco
zurückhaltend
Lie- ben, Hof- fen, Lie- ben, Hof- fen, und _ Ver- trau'n, Lie- ben,
Lie- ben, Hof- fen, Lie- ben, Hof- fen, und _ Ver- trau'n, ___ Lie- ben,
59
Hn. 1, 2
Tpt. 1
Hof- fen, und _ Ver- trau'n, Lie- ben, Hof- fen, und Ver-
Hof- fen, und Ver- trau'n, Lie- ben, Hof- fen, und Ver-

-trau'n, Lie- ben, Hof- fen, und Ver-

67
rit.
molto rit.
Breit, doch zart
Fl. 1, 2
Ob. 1, 2
Cl. 1, 2
Bn. 1, 2
Hn. 1, 2
Hn. 3, 4
Trb. 1, 2
Trb. 3
Tb.
pp
tr
rit.
molto rit.
Breit, doch zart
Vn. 1
Vn. 2
Va.
espress.
Clar.
-trau'n, und Ver- trau'n, ja Ver- trau'n!
Gom.
-trau'n, und Ver- trau'n, ja Ver- trau'n!
Vc.
Cb.
pizz.

335

No. 12. Terzett-Finale

337

338

339

340

341

35
C
[1]
Fl. 1, 2
Hn. 1, 2
Hn. 3, 4
Vn. 1
Vn. 2
Va.
Laura
Gom.
Vc.
Cb.
arco
pizz.
espress.
fort, die Ne- bel bald fort, die Ne- bel bald fort.
Ver- trau' mei- nem
38
Ob. 1, 2
Cl. 1, 2
Clar.
Vc. Cb.
Mein Herr und mein Hort, mein
Und nun auch
Wort, ver- trau' mei- nem Wort, ver-

343

46
[1]
Fl. 1, 2
[1]
Ob. 1, 2
1
Cl. 1, 2
p espress.
Bn. 1, 2
1
Hn. 1, 2
Hn. 3, 4
Vn. 1
pp
pizz.
Vn. 2
pizz.
Va.
Clar.
nen- nen, dies ängst- li- che Be- ben, dies
Laura
Es wird sich schon ge- ben dies Tren- nen, dies Bren- nen, doch jet- zo nur fort, doch jet- zo nur
Gom.
Le- ben, von dir mich zu tren- nen, zer-
Vc.
Cb.

345

56
Bn. 1, 2
Hn. 1, 2
Vn. 1
Vn. 2
Va.
Clar.
Laura
Gom.
Vc.
Cb.
p
espress.
lie- ber bei Dir hier am Ort, ja hier am Ort, leb'
Mi- nu- ten ver- ge- hen, hier län- ger zu ste- hen, ist ge- gen Ak-
Theu- re, den Schwur ich er- neu'- re, Du trau' mei-nem Wort, leb'
60
wohl, mein Lie- ber, wie blieb' ich lie- ber bei
-kord, Mi- nu- ten ver- geh'n, Mi- nu- ten ver- ge- hen, hier
wohl, du Theu- re, den Schwur ich er- neu'- re, ich

Wieder etwas vorwärts gehen

Clar.: Dir, hier am Ort, ich kann es nicht nen- nen, dies ängst- li- che

Laura: län- ger zu ste- hen, ist ge- gen Ak- kord, Mi- nu- ten ver-

Gom.: hal- te mein Wort! Von Dir mich zu tren- nen, zer- reißt mir das

348

Clar.: Be- ben, dies ängst- li- che Be- ben, _____ le- be wohl, o Du mein Le- ben,

Laura: -geh'n, hier län- ger zu ste- hen, hier län- ger zu ste- hen, hier län- ger zu ste- hen, ist ge- gen Ak-

Gom.: Le- ben, zer- reißt mein Le- ben, _____ le- be wohl, o le- be, _____

E
71
Ob. 1, 2
Hn. 1, 2
Vn. 1
Vn. 2
Va.
Clar.
Laura
Gom.
Vc.
Cb.
pp
sempre pp
divisi
arco
pizz.
le- be wohl!
-kord! Es wird sich schon ge- ben, dies Bren- nen, dies Be- ben, und jet- zo nur
le- be wohl!
f
74
Bn. 1, 2
rit.
Nachgeben!
1
p
solo
fort, nur fort, nur fort, nur fort!
Breit
Leb' wohl denn, du
espress.

350

351

84
Ob. 1, 2
Cl. 1, 2
1
Bn. 1, 2
Hn. 1, 2
solo
Vn. 1
Vn. 2
Va.
Clar.
le- be, le- - be,
Laura
ste- hen und jet- zo nur fort und sagt Euch
Gom.
Theu- re, le- - be
Vc.
pizz.
Cb.

87
Fl. 1, 2
a 2
p
Ob. 1, 2
a 2
p
Cl. 1, 2
p
Bn. 1, 2
[a 2]
p
Hn. 1, 2
1
p
Hn. 3, 4
p
Tpt. 1, 2
[1]
p
Vn. 1
p
Vn. 2
p
Va.
p
Clar.
le- be wohl, o le- be wohl, o le- be
Laura
le- be wohl, Mi- nu- ten ver- geh'n, hier län- ger zu
Gom.
wohl, den Eid ich er- neu'- re, den Eid ich er-
Vc.
p
Cb.
pizz.
p

90
a 2
Fl. 1, 2
a 2
Ob. 1, 2
Cl. 1, 2
[a 2]
Bn. 1, 2
1
Hn. 1, 2
[a 2]
Hn. 3, 4
[1]
Tpt. 1, 2
Vn. 1
Vn. 2
Va.
Clar.
wohl, o le- be wohl, o
Laura
steh'n, hier län- ger zu steh'n
Gom.
-neu'- re, ich hal- te mein Wort, ich
Vc.
Cb.

93
rit.
Fl. 1, 2
Ob. 1, 2
a 2
Cl. 1, 2
Bn. 1, 2
Hn. 1, 2
Hn. 3, 4
1
Tpt. 1, 2
mf
rit.
Vn. 1
Vn. 2
ff
Va.
ff
Clar.
le- be wohl, leb' wohl, leb'
Laura
und jet- zo nur fort, und jet- zo nur
Gom.
hal- te mein Wort, leb' wohl, leb'
[arco]
Vc.
[arco]
Cb.

Clar.: wohl!

Laura: fort!

Gom.: wohl!

99
Più mosso
accel.
a 2
Fl. 1, 2
Ob. 1, 2
Cl. 1, 2
Bn. 1, 2
Hn. 1, 2
Hn. 3, 4
Tpt. 1, 2
Trb. 3
Tb.
Timp.
Vn. 1
Vn. 2
Va.
Vc.
Cb.

Ende des II. Aufzugs

III. Aufzug
No. 13. Lied mit Chor

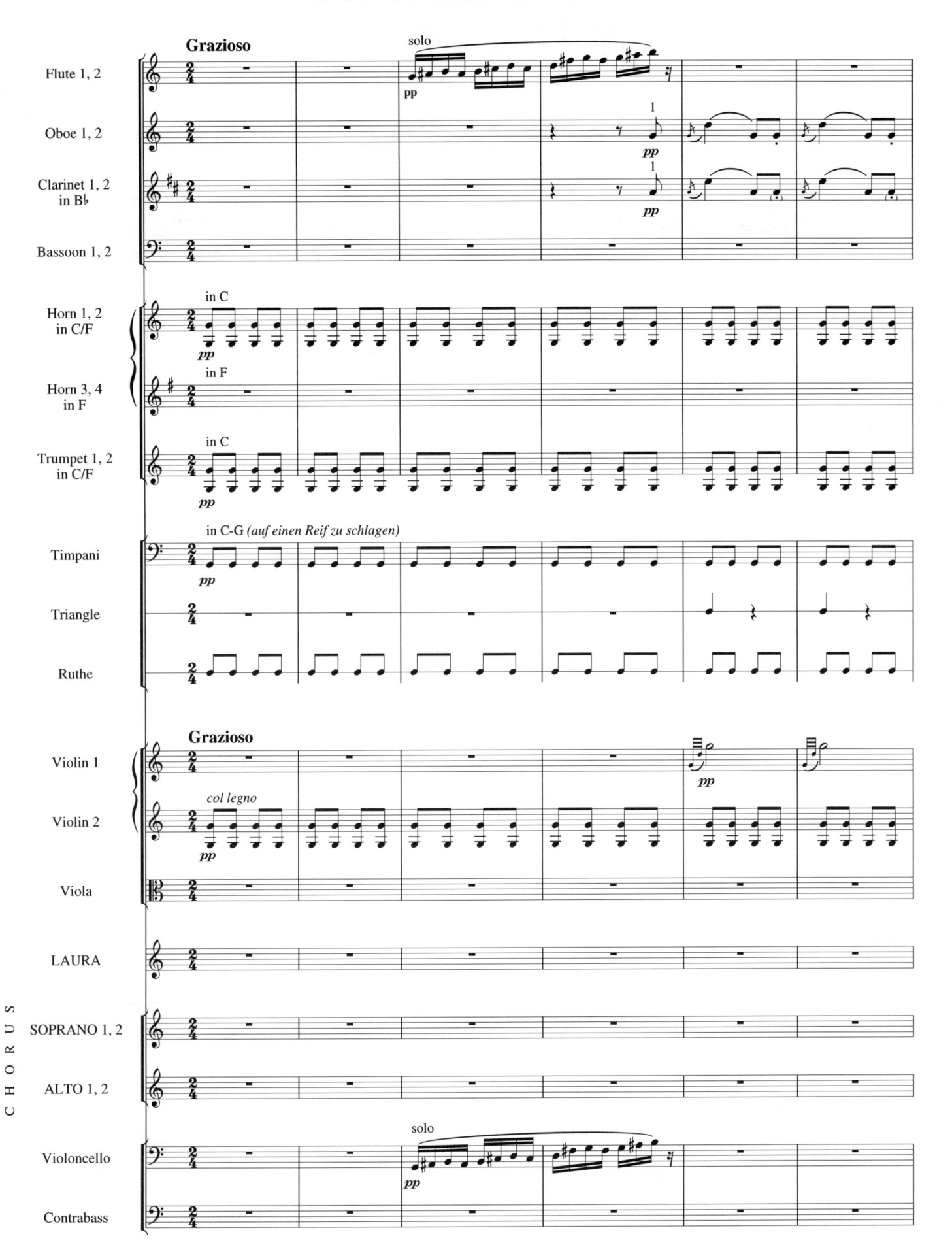

360

13
Fl. 1, 2
Ob. 1, 2
Cl. 1, 2
Bn. 1, 2
Hn. 1, 2
Tpt. 1, 2
Timp.
Ruthe
pp
Vn. 1
Vn. 2
Va.
Vc.
Cb.
tr

Schmücket die Halle mit Blüthen und Zweigen,

Ro- sen und Myr- then in sin- ni- gen Reih'n!

Schmü- cket die Hal- le mit Blü- then und Zwei- gen,

Ro- sen und Myr- then in sinn'- gen Reih'n, in sin- ni- gen Reih'n, in

sin- ni- gen Reih'n! ... Laßt aus dem

Laßt aus dem

367

368

369

370

76
Fl. 1, 2
Ob. 1, 2
Cl. 1, 2
Bn. 1, 2
Hn. 1, 2
Hn. 3, 4
Tpt. 1, 2
Timp.
Vn. 1
Vn. 2
Va.
Laura
S1
S2
A1
A2
Vc.
Cb.
a 2
tr
solo
in C-G
pizz.
(nicht riten.)
streut auf den Pfad ihm zum Hoch- zeits- al- tar, streut auf den Pfad _ ihm zum
streut auf den Pfad ihm zum Hoch- zeits- al- tar.
streut auf den Pfad ihm zum Hoch- zeits- al- tar.
dim.
pp

D
82
Fl. 1, 2
Ob. 1, 2
solo
Cl. 1, 2
Bn. 1, 2
Hn. 1, 2
Hn. 3, 4
Tpt. 1, 2
Timp.
Trgl.
Vn. 1
arco
Vn. 2
arco
Va.
arco
pizz.
Laura
Hoch- zeits- al- tar.
Schmü- cket die
S1
S2
Schmü- cket die
A1
A2
Schmü- cket die
Vc.
pizz.
Cb.

373

374

100
Fl. 1, 2
Ob. 1, 2
Cl. 1, 2
Bn. 1, 2
Hn. 1, 2
Tpt. 1, 2
(tr)
Timp.
Vn. 1
Vn. 2
Va.
Laura
-tig! Ei seht, wie _ wun- der- schön! Wun- der- schön! Wun- der-
S1
S2
-tig! Ei seht, wie _ wun- der- schön! Wun- der- schön! Wun- der-
A1
A2
-tig! Ei seht, wie wun- der- schön! Wun- der- schön! Wun- der-
Vc.
Cb.

376

113
Fl. 1, 2
Ob. 1, 2
Cl. 1, 2
Bn. 1, 2
[a 2]
Hn. 1, 2
Tpt. 1, 2
Timp.
Trgl.
Vn. 1
Vn. 2
Va.
Laura
S1
S2
A1
A2
Vc.
Cb.

No. 14. Duett

9
Ob. 1, 2
Cl. 1, 2
Bn. 1, 2
(tr)
Timp.
cresc.
Vn. 1
ff
Vn. 2
ff
Va.
ff
16
A
Cl. 1, 2
f
Bn. 1, 2
f
Hn. 1, 2
f
(tr)
[in C-G]
Timp.
ff
Vn. 1
Vn. 2
divisi
Va.
f
Gast.
f
Nun da sind wir, hier nicht
Ambr.
f
Nun da sind wir, hier nicht
Vc.
f
pizz.
Cb.
f

23
Cl. 1, 2
Bn. 1, 2
Hn. 1, 2
Vn. 1
Vn. 2
Va.
Gast.
e- ben scheint man Mü- he sich zu ge- ben, gro- ße Ehr' uns an- zu- thun!
Ambr.
e- ben scheint man Mü- he sich zu ge- ben, gro- ße Ehr' uns an- zu- thun!
Vc.
Cb.
29
Cl. 1, 2
Bn. 1, 2
Hn. 1, 2
Va.
Gast.
Nun da sind wir, hier nicht e- ben scheint man Mü- he sich zu ge- ben, gro- ße Ehr' _ uns _
Ambr.
Nun da sind wir, hier nicht e- ben scheint man Mü- he sich zu ge- ben, gro- ße Ehr' uns
Vc.
Cb.

381

Schlaf zu ruh'n.

Auch der Al- te, der vom Tho- re uns so höf- lich hier-her führ- te, lag wohl just auf ei- nem Oh- re, doch in sei- nem Lä- cheln spür- te ich ein freund- li- ches Ver- gnü- gen, ja in sei- nem Lä- cheln spür- te ich ein freund- li- ches Ver- gnü- gen!

Ei! Es wird sich Al- les fü- gen, har- ren

Ei! Es wird sich Al- les fü- gen, har- ren

71
Fl. 1, 2
Ob. 1, 2
Cl. 1, 2
Bn. 1, 2
[a 2]
Hn. 1, 2
Hn. 3, 4
Vn. 1
Vn. 2
Va.
pp
Gast.
wir ge- trost der Din- ge, die sich ber- gen hier im Hau- se,
Ambr.
wir ge- trost der Din- ge, die sich ber- gen hier im Hau- se,
Vc.
arco
pp
Cb.

harren wir getrost der Dinge, die sich bergen hier im Hause, daß das

81
Fl. 1, 2
Ob. 1, 2
Cl. 1, 2
Bn. 1, 2
a 2
Hn. 1, 2
p
Hn. 3, 4
[3]
p
Vn. 1
Vn. 2
Va.
Gast.
Werk _ ge- lin- ge.
Ambr.
Werk ge- lin- ge.
arco
Vc.
arco
Cb.

Kommt es nur zum Hoch-zeits- schmau-se, da will ich recht lu- stig sprin-gen, da will

92
Fl. 1, 2
Ob. 1, 2
Cl. 1, 2
Bn. 1, 2
Hn. 1, 2
Hn. 3, 4
Timp.
Vn. 1
Vn. 2
Va.
Ambr.
Vc.
[1]
tr
pp
a 2
[a 2]
f
p
pizz.
arco
[arco]
ich recht lu- stig sprin-gen, da will ich recht lu- stig sprin- gen!

Ka- stag- net- ten hör' ich klin- gen, Dum trr um trr um trr um tum, Flöt' und

390

109
Picc. 1, 2
Ob. 1, 2
Cl. 1, 2
Bn. 1, 2
Hn. 1, 2
Hn. 3, 4
Tpt. 1, 2
Timp.
Trgl.
Tamb.
Cast.
Vn. 1
Vn. 2
Va.
Ambr.
Vc.
Cb.
[a 2]
[a 2]
pp
p
p
p
di del dum di del du del di del du del di del du del di del dum di del du del di del du del di del du del

392

393

-legen, frischen Muthes vorwärts nun! Jeder

137
Hn. 1, 2
Vn. 1
Vn. 2
Va.
Gast.
Schwank kommt ja ge- le- gen, je- der Schwank kommt ja ge- le- gen uns'- rer fröh- li-
Ambr.
Schwank kommt ja ge- le- gen, je- der Schwank kommt ja ge- le- gen uns'- rer fröh- li-
Vc. Cb.
Cb.
142
G
Hn. 1, 2
Vn. 1
Vn. 2
Va.
Gast.
-chen Na- tur. Nur ein Thor der Zu- kunft
Ambr.
-chen Na- tur. Nur ein Thor der Zu- kunft
Vc. Cb.
Cb.

147
Vn. 1
Vn. 2
Va.
Gast.
harrt, Wei- sen lacht die Ge- gen- wart, Wei- - sen lacht die Ge- gen-
Ambr.
harrt, Wei- sen lacht die Ge- gen- wart, Wei- - sen lacht die Ge- gen-
Vc. Cb.
arco
Cb.
154
H
Cl. 1, 2
mf
[a 2]
Vn. 1
Vn. 2
Va.
Gast.
-wart, Wei- - sen lacht die Ge- gen- wart! Nur ein Thor der Zu- kunft
Ambr.
-wart, Wei- - sen lacht die Ge- gen- wart! Nur ein Thor der Zu- kunft
Vc. Cb.
mf
Cb.
mf

harrt, Weisen lacht die Gegenwart! Nur ein Thor der Zukunft harrt, Weisen

harrt, Weisen lacht die Gegenwart! Nur ein Thor der Zukunft harrt, Weisen

lacht die Gegenwart!

lacht die Gegenwart!

No. 15. Terzettino
(Canon)

*Dieses ganze Stück ist von den Sängern im leichtesten Parlando auszuführen.

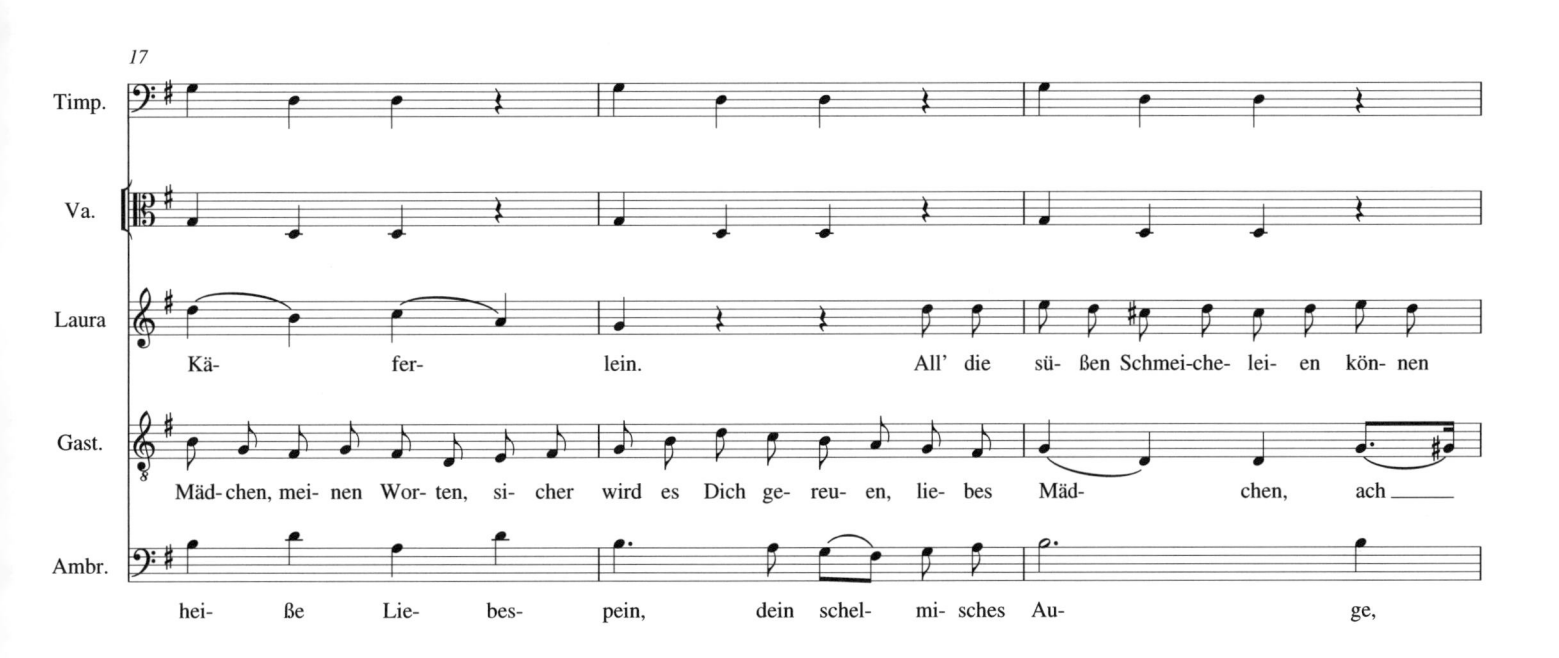

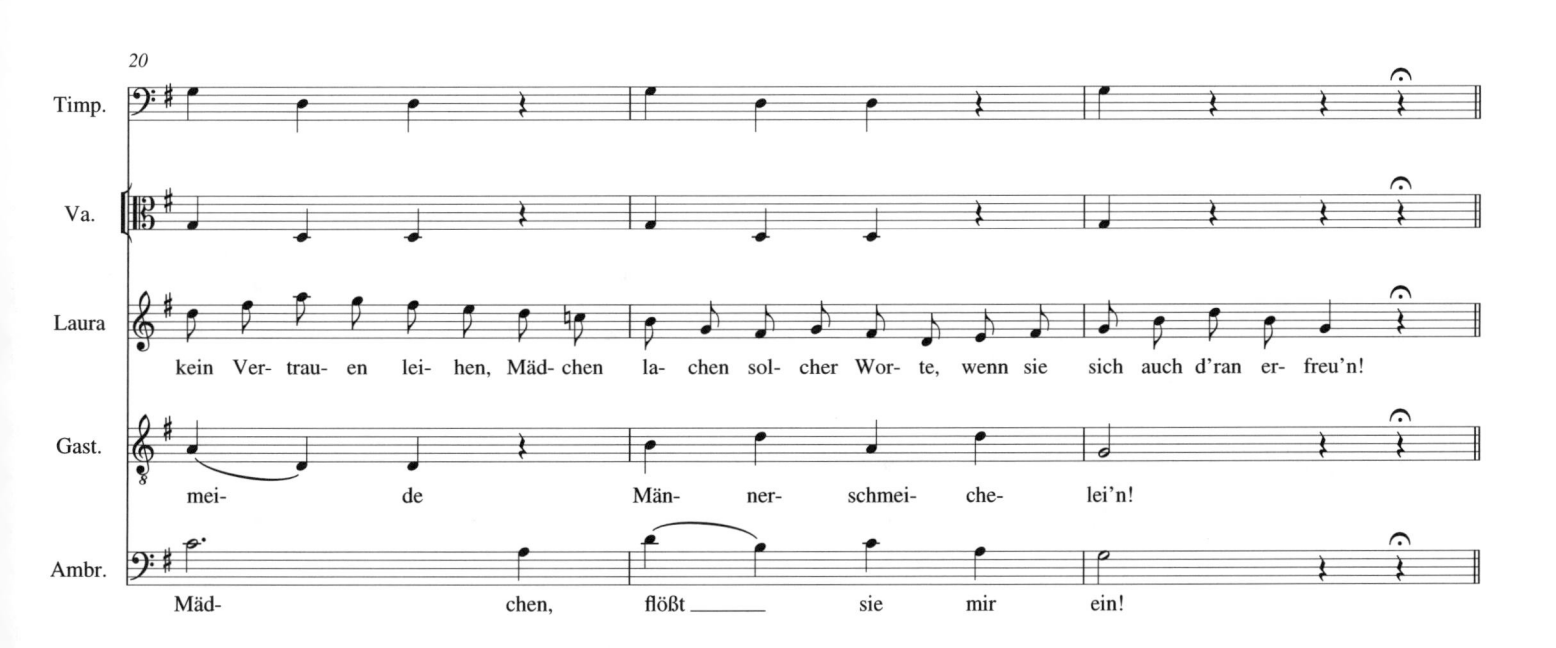

Laura: -lei'n, wie Rosen die Schwüre bunter Käferlein. All' die süßen Schmeicheleien können kein Vertrauen leihen, Mädchen lachen solcher Worte, wenn sie sich auch d'ran erfreu'n!

Gast.: ein. Statt der süßen Schmeicheleien hörst Du "Papa, Mama" schreien, glaube, Mädchen, meinen Worten, sicher wird es Dich gereuen, liebes Mädchen, ach meide Männerschmeichelei'n!

Ambr.: wird es Dich gereuen, liebes Mädchen, ich leide heiße Liebespein, dein schelmisches Auge, Mädchen, flößt sie mir ein!

23
Bn. 1
Timp.
Ambr.
Vc.
p
p
Mäd- chen, ich lei- de
pizz.
pp
27
Bn. 1
Timp.
Va.
Gast.
Ambr.
Vc.
pp
Mäd- chen, ach mei- de
hei- ße Lie- bes- pein, dein schel- mi- sches Au- ge, Mäd- chen,
31
Bn. 1
Timp.
Vn. 1
Va.
Laura
Gast.
Ambr.
Vc.
Cb.
pizz.
pp
(Gaston parodirend)
"Mäd- chen, ach
Män- ner- schmei- che- lei'n, die ko- sen- den Wor- te,
flößt sie mir ein. Nicht nur sü- ße Schmei- che- lei- en will dies
pizz.
pp

meide Männerschmeichelei'n, die kosenden weiche Herz Dir weihen, glaube, Mädchen, meinen Worten, nimmer wird es Dich gereuen, liebes

Mädchen, schläfern Dich ein. Statt der

Worte, Mädchen, schläfern Dich
süßen Schmeicheleien hörst Du "Papa, Mama" schreien, glaube, Mädchen, meinen Worten, sicher
Mädchen, ich leide heiße Liebes-

40
Bn. 1
Timp.
Vn. 1
Va.
Laura
zu Ambrosio, ihn verspottend
ein!" Ta ta ta ta ta ta ta ta ta ta ta ta ta ta ta ta ta ta
Gast.
wird es Dich ge- reu- en, lie- bes Mäd- chen, ach mei- de
Ambr.
-pein, dein schel- mi- sches Au- ge, Mäd- chen,
Vc.
Cb.
43
Bn. 1
Timp.
Vn. 1
Va.
Laura
läuft fort
ta ta ta ta ta ta ta ta ta ta ta ta ta!
Gast.
Män- ner- schmei- che- lei'n!
Ambr.
flößt sie mir ein!
Vc.
Cb.

No. 16. Ariette

*Ambrosio parodirt seinen eignen Zorn, dann schlägt er ein Schnippchen.

*Gaston spottend: "Ha, welch ein furchtbarer Zorn."

9
Fl. 1, 2
Ob. 1, 2
Cl. 1, 2
Bn. 1, 2
Hn. 1, 2
Hn. 3, 4
Tpt. 1, 2
Timp.
B. Drum
Ambr.
Vc.
Cb.
(gestopft)
[offen]
schwer
[schwer]
Ein
13
Allegro vivace
Ob. 1, 2
Bn. 1, 2
Vn. 1
Vn. 2
Va.
Ambr.
Vc. Cb.
Mäd- chen ver- lo- ren, was macht man sich d'raus? Man
muß in der Lie- be nicht ein- sei- tig sein. Man
rath' Euch Ihr Män- ner schwört nie ei- nen Eid! Ich

17
Ob. 1, 2
Bn. 1, 2
Hn. 1, 2
Hn. 3, 4
Vn. 1
Vn. 2
Va.
Ambr.
Vc.
Cb.
[a 2]
p
A Gemächlich
Gemächlich
pizz.
arco
pp
comodo
sucht sich in Spa- nien ein' An- de- re aus! Und
hält es am be- sten mit Zwei- en und Drei'n. Denn
rath' Euch als Ken- ner, sonst fängt Euch die Maid! Denn
22
string.
mf
Vc. Cb.
täuscht uns auch die- se was liegt denn da- ran? Es kommt heut' zu
kränkt uns die Ei- ne wie leicht hat man's dann, man war- tet ganz
wird sie Euch lä- stig, so sit- zet Ihr d'ran, es läßt Euch kein

407

408

la la la ein Schock auf den Mann! Mann! La la la la la la la la la la la la
la la la bis sie kommt da- ran! an! La la la la la la la la la la la la
la la la leicht los ih- ren Mann! Mann! La la la la la la la la la la la la

la — la la — ein Schock auf den Mann! Ein Schock auf den
la — la la — bis sie kommt da- ran! Bis sie kommt da-
la — la la — leicht los ih- ren Mann! Leicht los ih- ren

Mann!
-ran!
Mann!

2. Man
3. Ich

No. 17. Rondo-Terzett

5
Fl. 1, 2
Ob. 1, 2
Cl. 1, 2
Bn. 1, 2
Hn. 1, 2
Vn. 1
Vn. 2
Va.
Gom.
Vc.
Cb.
p zart
[1]
treu' be-wahr-et Ehr' und ho-hen Sinn, Ihr woll-tet tren- nen zwei treu-e Her- zen, rein-ste
9
rit.
a tempo
arco
espress.
Lie- be op- fern da- hin? Ver- möcht' mein hei-ßes Fleh'n Euch zu be- we- gen, Ihr trügt in

13
A
[1]
[1]
[a 2]
Fl. 1, 2
Ob. 1, 2
Cl. 1, 2
Bn. 1, 2
Hn. 1, 2
Vn. 1
Vn. 2
Va.
Gom.
Vc.
Cb.
espress.
ausdrucksvoll
pizz.
Euch den schön-sten Lohn!
O gebt Ge- hör den bes-sern Trie- ben, gönnt mir, was
17
[1]
rubato
Ob. 1, 2
Bn. 1, 2
Vn. 1
Vn. 2
Va.
Gom.
Vc.
Cb.
zart
sich zu _ mir ge- wandt,
das höch-ste Gut, das mir ge- blie- ben:

414

*Von diesen Quintolen ist immer die *erste* Note heftig zu betonen, die anderen 4 Noten zierlich und *p* zu spielen.

weichen auf freier Bahn? Gebt acht, daß Ihr Euch nur nicht

416

könn- te Euch zei- gen, wie man Spaß ver- steht! Ich hal- te Cla-

-ris- sa, ich hal- te sie fest, ich halt' sie

52
C
Fl. 1, 2
Ob. 1, 2
Cl. 1, 2
Bn. 1, 2
Hn. 1, 2
Hn. 3, 4
Vn. 1
Vn. 2
Va.
Gast.
Ambr.
Vc.
Cb.
a 2
fest!
Ja, al- le tau-send Don-ner-wet-ter, wie der prah-len kann! Halt' sie nur fest,
divisi
pizz.
arco

halt' sie nur fest, daß sie Dich nicht los- läßt!

Tempo I
Cl. 1, 2
Bn. 1, 2
Hn. 1, 2
Tempo I
Vn. 1
Vn. 2
Va.
Gom.
Ward je ein zar- tes hol-des Re- gen se- lig- ster Lieb' Euch be-
Vc.
Cb.
Fl. 1, 2
Ob. 1, 2
Cl. 1, 2
Bn. 1, 2
Hn. 1, 2
Hn. 3, 4
Vn. 1
Vn. 2
Va.
Gom.
-wußt, hat je in hei- ßen, mächt'-gen Schlä- gen das Herz Euch ge-klopft in der
Vc.
Cb.

72
rit.
a tempo
Fl. 1, 2
Ob. 1, 2
Cl. 1, 2
Bn. 1, 2
Hn. 1, 2
Hn. 3, 4
Vn. 1
Vn. 2
Va.
Gom.
Vc.
Cb.
[1]
[a 2]
[3]
espress.
Brust, so müßt Ihr mei-nes In-nern Drang ver- ste- hen, er-ken-nen mei- ne höch-ste Noth!

Bei je-der Hoff-nung Eu- res Le- bens, bei Eu-rer Ah- nen Wap- pen-schild, beim Sie- ge Eu-res kühn-sten

424

Nun denn wohl- an, mein Herr Rit- ters- mann! Ich tre- te zu-rück, Euch be- gün- stigt das Glück! Ich wün- sche zur Hoch- zeit Euch

426

108
Fl. 1, 2
Ob. 1, 2
Cl. 1, 2
Bn. 1, 2
Hn. 1, 2
Hn. 3, 4
Tpt. 1, 2
Timp.
Vn. 1
Vn. 2
Va.
Gom.
Gast.
Ambr.
Vc.
Cb.
a 2
p
fp
sim.
mf
pizz.
f
Er tritt zu- rück, ü- ber- schwäng-lich' Glück, welch'
Nun denn wohl- an, mein Herr Rit- ters- mann! Was habt Ihr für
Mei- net- we- gen Glück und Se- gen; glück- li-cher Mann, der sie ge- wann! Halt' sie nur

428

118
Fl. 1, 2
p
Ob. 1, 2
p
Cl. 1, 2
5
Bn. 1, 2
Hn. 1, 2
fp
[sim.]
Hn. 3, 4
Tpt. 1, 2
Vn. 1
Vn. 2
(tr)
Va.
tr
Gom.
-ris- sa ist mein, Cla- ris- sa, Cla- ris- sa wird se- lig am
Gast.
viel Ver- gnü- gen, Cla- ris- sa wird se- lig am Her- zen Euch
Ambr.
kann da- ran lie- gen? Es kann doch nur Ei- ner von Bei- den sie
Vc.
arco
Cb.

430

431

Fl. 1, 2
a 2
Ob. 1, 2
a 2
Cl. 1, 2
Bn. 1, 2
Hn. 1, 2
Hn. 3, 4
Tpt. 1, 2
a 2
Timp.
Vn. 1
Vn. 2
Va.
Gom.
-te sie fest!
Gast.
-tet sie fest!
Ambr.
steht doch fest!
Vc.
Cb.

138
Picc. 1, 2
a 2
f
Picc. 1, 2
Ob. 1, 2
a 2
Cl. 1, 2
a 2
Bn. 1, 2
a 2
Hn. 1, 2
a 2
Hn. 3, 4
a 2
Tpt. 1, 2
a 2
Timp.
f
Vn. 1
Vn. 2
Va.
Vc.
Cb.

No. 18. Chor

435

10
Vn. 1
Vn. 2
Va.
S
A
T
B
Vc.
Cb.
(Einige)
pp
Je- ner?
ist es?
Ja!
(And're)
Nein, der And'-re!
(And're)
Frei- lich!
(And're)
Frei- lich!
(And're)
Nein, der And'-re!
13
A
Fl. 1, 2
Ob. 1, 2
Cl. 1, 2
Bn. 1, 2
Hn. 1, 2
ff
p
hervortretend
espress.
pp
Ja!
Ja!
Ja!
Ja!
Still doch, still, da naht sie schon!
pizz.
pp

437

438

22
Fl. 1, 2
Ob. 1, 2
Cl. 1, 2
Bn. 1, 2
arco
Vn. 1
Vn. 2
Va.
S
schaut, was wird wohl Cla- ris- sa sa- gen, wenn sie
A
schaut, was wird wohl Cla- ris- sa sa- gen, wenn sie
T
schaut, was wird wohl Cla- ris- sa sa- gen, wenn sie
B
schaut, was wird wohl Cla- ris- sa sa- gen, wenn sie
Vc.
Cb.

B
25
Fl. 1, 2
Ob. 1, 2
Cl. 1, 2
Bn. 1, 2
Tpt. 1, 2
pp
Vn. 1
pp
Vn. 2
arco
Va.
arco
S
den _ Ver- lob- ten _ schaut? Ei- nen sol- chen Mann ge- win- nen, ist ein
A
den _ Ver- lob- ten schaut? Ei- nen sol- chen Mann ge- win- nen, ist ein
T
den _ Ver- lob- ten schaut? Ei- nen sol- chen Mann ge- win- nen, ist ein
B
den _ Ver- lob- ten schaut? Ei- nen sol- chen Mann ge- win- nen, ist ein
Vc.
arco
Cb.
arco

selt'- nes, gro- ßes Glück! Kann ein Mäd- chen sich be-

442

443

444

41
Fl. 1, 2
Ob. 1, 2
Cl. 1, 2
Bn. 1, 2
Hn. 1, 2
Hn. 3, 4
Tpt. 1, 2
Timp.
Vn. 1
Vn. 2
Va.
S
Stun- de! Heil die- ses Haus!
A
Stun- de! Heil die- ses Haus!
T
Glück, Se- gen und Heil auf die- ses Haus!
B
schon! Glück, Se- gen und Heil auf die- ses Haus!
Vc.
Cb.

D
45
Fl. 1, 2
Ob. 1, 2
Cl. 1, 2
Bn. 1, 2
Hn. 1, 2
Hn. 3, 4
Tpt. 1, 2
Trb. 1, 2
Trb. 3
Tb.
Timp.
Vn. 1
Vn. 2
Va.
S
A
T
B
Vc.
Cb.
a 2
in F-C-B♭
(Don Pantaleone führt die festlich geschmückte Clarissa herein)
Seht, sie naht! Heil!
Seht, sie naht! Heil!
Seht, sie naht, seht, sie naht! Heil!
Seht, sie naht, seht, sie naht, seht, sie naht! Heil!

Heil und höchstes Glück! Heil Clarissa, Panta-

448

58
Fl. 1, 2
Ob. 1, 2
Cl. 1, 2
Bn. 1, 2
Hn. 1, 2
Hn. 3, 4
Tpt. 1, 2
Tpt. 3
Trb. 1, 2
Trb. 3
Tb.
Timp.
Vn. 1
Vn. 2
Va.
S
schenkt! Seid ge- grüßt, seid ge- grüßt!
A
schenkt! Seid ge- grüßt, seid ge- grüßt!
T
schenkt! Seid ge- grüßt, seid ge- grüßt! Will-
B
schenkt! Seid ge- grüßt, seid ge- grüßt! Will-
Vc.
Cb.

62
Fl. 1, 2
Ob. 1, 2
Cl. 1, 2
Bn. 1, 2
Hn. 1, 2
Hn. 3, 4
Tpt. 1, 2
Tpt. 3
Trb. 1, 2
Trb. 3
Tb.
Timp.
Vn. 1
Vn. 2
Va.
S
A
T
B
Vc.
Cb.
a 2
ff
tr
Will- kom- men!
Will- kom- men, will- kom- men!
-kom- men, will- kom- men, will- kom- men!
-kom- men, will- kom- men, will- kom- men!

No. 19. Mädchenlied

A
Fl. 1
Ob. 1, 2
Cl. 1, 2
Bn. 1, 2
Hn. 1
Trgl.
Vn. 1
Vn. 2
Va.
S
A1
A2
Vc.
pizz.
arco
Blu- men, mit duf-ten-den Blü- then, mit lieb- li-chen
Blu- men, mit duf-ten-den Blü- then, mit lieb- li-chen

453

18
B
Fl. 1
Ob. 1, 2
pp
Cl. 1, 2
Bn. 1, 2
pp
Hn. 1
Trgl.
divisi
2 solo violins
Vn. 1
pp
pp
Vn. 2
pp
pizz.
Va.
pizz.
S
Sie win- den der Hol- den
A1
A2
Sie win- den der Hol- den
arco
Solo Vc.
pp
Vc.
pp
pizz.
Cb.
pizz.

die bräut-li-chen Zwei-ge, frisch grü-nen-der Myr-the in's lo-cki-ge Haar,

30
C
Fl. 1
Ob. 1, 2
Cl. 1, 2
Bn. 1, 2
Tpt. 1
Solo Vn.
Vn. 1
Vn. 2
Solo Va.
Va.
S
— sie win- den der Hol- den frisch grü- nen- der Myr- the in's
A1
A2
— sie win- den der Hol- den frisch grü- nen- der Myr- the in's
Solo Vc.
Vc.
Cb.
pizz.
pizz.

lo- ckige Haar, frisch grü- nen- der Myr- the in's lo- ckige Haar.

458

459

No. 20. Finale A

461

Pinto schreitet gewichtig und aufgeblasen durch den Haupteingang herein. Pantaleone tritt ihm würdevoll entgegen.

Pant.: Was wollt Ihr? Wer

Fl. 1, 2
Ob. 1, 2
Cl. 1, 2
Bn. 1, 2
Hn. 1, 2
Hn. 3, 4
Tpt. 1, 2
Trb. 1, 2
Trb. 3 Tb.
Timp.
Vn. 1
Vn. 2
Va.
Gast.
(beiseite)
Nun, ich wa- sche mei- ne
Pant.
seid Ihr? Was sucht Ihr? Was wollt Ihr? Wer seid Ihr? Was sucht Ihr?
CHORUS
S
A
T
B
Was wollt Ihr? Wer seid Ihr? Was sucht Ihr?
Vc. Cb.

463

464

22
Maestoso
Fl. 1, 2
Ob. 1, 2
Cl. 1, 2
Bn. 1, 2
Hn. 1, 2
Hn. 3, 4
Tpt. 1, 2
Trb. 1, 2
Timp.
Vn. 1
Vn. 2
Va.
Pinto
S
A
T
B
Vc.
Cb.
a 2
Und ich su- che mei- ne Braut, ja, ich su- che mei- ne Braut, ja, ich
-se- ca?

27
B
Nicht eilen!
a 2
tr
Fl. 1, 2
Ob. 1, 2
Cl. 1, 2
Bn. 1, 2
p
Hn. 1, 2
Hn. 3, 4
Trb. 3
Tb.
Tb.
pp
Cym.
ppp
Vn. 1
Vn. 2
Va.
Gom.
Dies wär'
Pinto
su- che mei- ne Braut, denn ich bin Pin- to, Don Pin- to de Fon- se- ca!
[Der Chor] scharf im Rhythmus
ppp (flüsternd)
S
Dies wär'
A
Dies wär' Pin- to de Fon-
T
Dies wär' Pin- to de Fon- se- ca?
B
Die- ser wä- re
Vc.
Cb.

31
Fl. 1, 2
Ob. 1, 2
Cl. 1, 2
Bn. 1, 2
Trb. 3
Tb.
(tr)
Cym.
Vn. 1
Vn. 2
Va.
Clar.
p
Was will die- ser di- cke Mann? Wie? Die- ser wär' ist's er- hört, ist's er-
Laura
p
Was will die- ser di- cke Mann? Wie? Die- ser wär' ist's er- hört, ist's er-
Gom.
Pin- to, dies wär' Pin- to? Dies wär' Pin- to de Fon-
Pant.
p
Dies ein Pin- to de Fon-
Pinto
S
Pin- to? Er ist toll! Nur fort, hin- aus! Dies wär' Pin- to de Fon- se- ca! Er ist toll, nur fort, hin-
A
-se- ca? Er ist toll! Dies ein Pin- to de Fon- se- ca! Er ist toll, nur fort, hin-aus, nur fort, hin-
T
Er ist toll! Hin-aus, nur fort, hin- aus! Fort, hin- aus! Dies ein Pin- to de Fon-se- ca, fort, hin-
B
Pin- to, was? Er ist wohl toll! Fort, hin- aus! Dies ein Pin- to de Fon-se- ca! Fort, hin-
Vc.
Cb.
pp

34
Etwas zurückhaltend
a 2
pp
Fl. 1, 2
Ob. 1, 2
Cl. 1, 2
Bn. 1, 2
Trb. 3
Tb.
Tb.
Cym.
(tr)
Etwas zurückhaltend
pizz.
pp
Vn. 1
Vn. 2
Va.
Clar.
-hört: Pin- to! Pin- to! Pin- to!
Laura
-hört: Pin- to! Pin- to! Pin- to!
Gom.
-se- ca? Pin- to! Pin- to! Pin- to!
Pant.
-se- ca? Pin- to! Pin- to! Pin- to!
Pinto
S
-aus! Er wär' Pin- to de Fon- se- ca! Dies wär' Pin- to de Fon- se- ca?
A
-aus! Er wär' Pin- to de Fon- se- ca! Dies wär' Pin- to de Fon-
T
-aus! Er wär' Pin- to de Fon- se- ca! Dies wär' Pin- to de Fon- se- ca?
B
-aus! Er wär' Pin- to de Fon- se- ca! Dies wär' Pin- to de Fon-
Vc.
Cb.

469

su-che mei- ne Braut, denn ich bin Pin- to, Pin- to de Fon-se- ca und Cla-ris- sens an- ver-lob- ter Bräu- ti-

D
46
Vorwärts
Fl. 1, 2
Ob. 1, 2
Cl. 1, 2
Bn. 1, 2
Hn. 1, 2
Hn. 3, 4
Trb. 3
Tb.
Timp.
Vorwärts
Vn. 1
Vn. 2
Va.
[divisi]
Clar.
Die- ser wär' mein Bräu- ti- gam?
Laura
Dies Cla-ris- sens Bräu- ti- gam?
Gom.
Na, ein schö- ner Bräu- ti- gam, ja, für-wahr!
Pant.
Die- ser Schur- ke! Die- ser Schur- ke!
Pinto
-gam!
S
Die- ser wär', die- ser wär' ihr Bräu- ti- gam? Dies Don
A
Was? Ihr Bräu- ti- gam? Dies Don Pin- to
T
Dies Cla-ris- sens An- ver- lob- ter, dies Cla-ris- sens Bräu- ti- gam? Dies Don Pin- to
B
Die- ser wär' Cla-ris- sens Bräu- ti- gam, dies Cla-ris- sens Braü- ti- gam? Dies Don
[divisi]
Vc.
Cb.

49
Allegro moderato
Fl. 1, 2
[cresc.
ff
Ob. 1, 2
cresc.
ff
Cl. 1, 2
ff
Bn. 1, 2
ff
Hn. 1, 2
ff
Hn. 3, 4
ff
Tpt. 1, 2
f
Trb. 3
Tb.
f
(tr)
in D-B
Timp.
f
Allegro moderato
Vn. 1
cresc.
ff
Vn. 2
ff
Va.
ff
(Pinto geht mit plumpen Geberden auf Clarissa zu)
Pinto
S
Pin- to, dies Don Pin- to und Cla-ris- sens Bräu- ti- gam?
cresc.
A
de Fon- se- ca und Cla-ris- sens Bräu- ti- gam?
cresc.
T
de Fon- se- ca und Cla-ris- sens Bräu- ti- gam?
B
Pin- to, dies Don Pin- to und Cla-ris- sens Braü- ti- gam?
Vc.
cresc.
ff
Cb.
cresc.
ff

473

Sap-per- lot! Sap-per- lot! Ihr seid zum Ver- stand ver-

58
E
[1]
Fl. 1, 2
Ob. 1, 2
Cl. 1, 2
Bn. 1, 2
Hn. 1, 2
Hn. 3, 4
Vn. 1
Vn. 2
Va.
Gast.
Pinto
Solo Vc.
Vc.
Cb.
mf
p
pp
pizz.
(beiseite zu Ambrosio)
Schau' doch hin, was er ge-lernt!
-lie- ren, vor Ent- zü- cken bin ich todt!

476

(mit vor Aufregung überschlagender Stimme)

Pinto: Sap-per-lot! _____ Ich bin todt! _____ Vor Ent- zü- cken bin ich

478

71
Bn. 1, 2
Trb. 3
Tb.
Tb.
Timp.
Cym.
Vn. 1
Vn. 2
Va.
Clar.
Laura
Ambr.
Pant.
S
A
T
B
Vc.
Cb.
tr
p
pp
pizz.
arco
ppp (flüsternd)
Was be- ginnt er? Was er-
Was be- ginnt er? Was er-
lo- ser Mann!
Was thut der ar- me
Nun ver-liert er den Ver-
Den Ver- stand ver- lie- ren, vor Ent- zü- cken ist er
Den Ver-stand will er ver- lie- ren, vor Ent- zü- cken ist er
Soll mans wirk- lich glau- ben, vor Ent- zü- cken ist er todt?

Etwas zurückhaltend
74
[4]
Hn. 3, 4
Trb. 3
Tb.
Tb.
ppp
Timp.
(tr)
Cym.
(tr)
Etwas zurückhaltend
Vn. 1
Vn. 2
Va.
Clar.
-sinnt er? Was ver- liert er? Den Ver- stand?
Laura
-sinnt er? Was ver- liert er? Den Ver- stand?
Ambr.
pp
Pin- to!
Pant.
Tropf? Was spukt in sei- nem Kopf?
S
-stand! Habt Ihr's ge- hört? Und vor Ent- zü- cken ist er todt! Ar- mer Pin- to
A
todt! Den Ver-stand will er ver- lie- ren, vor Ent- zü- cken ist er todt! Ar- mer
T
todt! Den Ver-stand gar ver- lie- ren, vor Ent- zü- cken ist er todt! Ar- mer Pin- to
B
Und gar den Ver-stand noch ver- lie- ren, vor Ent- zü- cken ist er todt! Ar- mer
Vc.
Cb.

481

482

*Dieser Taktwechsel ist nur ein nothgedrungener Behelf für den Dirigenten eine Temponüance auszudrücken: im 1. Takt ist das 3. Viertel, im 2. Takt das 5. Viertel etwas zu beschleunigen, sodaß die beiden vorhergehenden Takttheile wie durch kurze Halte verlängert erscheinen.

91
Fl. 1, 2
Ob. 1, 2
Bn. 1, 2
Hn. 3, 4
Vn. 1
Vn. 2
Va.
Pinto
(ganz verwirrt)
ho- len, ma-che ich mich auf die Soh- len, e- he mich der Teu- fel
Vc.
Cb.
95
H
[1]
Fl. 1, 2
Ob. 1, 2
Bn. 1, 2
Vn. 1
Vn. 2
Va.
Ambr.
(höhnend beiseite)
Ach, das klingt doch gar zu herr-lich!
Pinto
(sich den Schweiß abwischend)
ho- le! Gott, das ist doch
Vc.
Cb.

484

485

106
Fl. 1, 2
Ob. 1, 2
Cl. 1, 2
Bn. 1, 2
Hn. 1, 2
Tpt. 1, 2
Trb. 3
Tb.
Vn. 1
Vn. 2
Va.
Gast.
Ambr.
Pinto
Vc.
Cb.
a 2
p
cresc.
[cresc.]
tr
hei- ter, 's geht recht fein, _ 's geht recht hei- ter, lie- ber, klei- ner, lust'- ger Pin- to, Pin- to, Pin- to, Pin- to,
-nah', seht doch nur den dum- men Töl- pel da, er dau- ert mich bei- nah', seht doch nur den dum- men
schön, ich bin toll ganz vor Ent- zü- cken, daß Sie

487

(mit Entschluß) bitt' ich *(schreiend)* ei- nen Schmatz!

Alle brechen in lautes Gelächter aus und zwar so, daß der Anfang desselben gerade auf das 2. Viertel des mit ⌐⌐ ⌐⌐ bezeichneten Taktes fällt.

489

dürf- te sich der Hol- den!

dürf- te sich in Hul- den ei- ner Da- me hold und

123
Fl. 1, 2
Ob. 1, 2
[1]
p
Cl. 1, 2
Bn. 1, 2
2
p
Hn. 1, 2
p
Vn. 1
Vn. 2
Va.
Gom.
Nein, das werd' ich nim-mer dul- den, nein, nein, nein, nein, daß ein sol- cher fre- cher
Gast.
licht! Nein, das darf kein Rit- ter dul- den, nein, nein, nein,
Pant.
Nein, das darf kein Va- ter
Vc.
mf
Cb.

J
127
[1]
Fl. 1, 2
[1]
Ob. 1, 2
pp
Cl. 1, 2
pp
2
Bn. 1, 2
pp
Hn. 1, 2
Hn. 3, 4
p
Tpt. 1, 2
pizz.
Vn. 1
p
pizz.
Vn. 2
p
pizz.
Va.
p
Gom.
Wicht, sich na- he _ mei- ner Da- me hold und licht!
Gast.
nein; nein, das darf kein Rit- ter dul- den, nein, nein, nein, nein!
Pant.
dul- den, nein, das duld' ich nim- mer- mehr!
p (kichernd)
pp sempre
S
Welch' ein Pin- to! Was, ein Pin- to! Welch' ein
p (kichernd)
pp [sempre]
A
Welch' ein Pin- to! Was, ein Pin- to! Welch' ein
p (kichernd)
pp [sempre]
T
Welch' ein Pin- to! Was, ein Pin- to! Welch' ein
p (kichernd)
pp [sempre]
B
Welch' ein Pin- to! Was, ein Pin- to! Welch' ein
pizz.
Vc.
p
Cb.

130
Nicht eilen!
Fl. 1, 2
a 2
pp
Ob. 1, 2
Cl. 1, 2
Bn. 1, 2
a 2
Hn. 1, 2
p
Hn. 3, 4
a 2
Tpt. 1, 2
a 2
pp
Nicht eilen!
Vn. 1
arco
8va
p espress.
Vn. 2
arco
p espress.
Va.
Clar.
f (hervortretend)
O welch' ein
Laura
f
Ei! _ Das
Gom.
f
Nein, nicht län- ger _ will ich's tra- gen, o Du
p
Gast.
f (beiseite)
Die- ser Spaß ist zum Ent- zü- cken, nie- mals könnt' es _ bes- ser glü- cken, o Du
p
Ambr.
f
Die- ser Spaß ist zum Ent- zü- cken, doch ist's Zeit, sich bald zu
p
Pant.
p
Nun hab' ich _
S
di- cker, lust'-ger Pin- to! Den Ver- stand will er ver- lie- ren! Ei, wo mag er ihn nur spü- ren?
A
di- cker, lust'-ger Pin- to! Den Ver- stand will er ver- lie- ren! Ei, wo mag er ihn nur spü- ren? Seht das
T
di- cker, lust'-ger Pin- to! Den Ver- stand will er ver- lie- ren! Ei, wo mag er ihn nur spü- ren? Seht das
B
di- cker, lust'-ger Pin- to! Den Ver- stand will er ver- lie- ren! Ei, wo mag er ihn nur spü- ren?
Vc.
arco
Cb.
pizz.
p

133
a 2
Fl. 1, 2
Ob. 1, 2
Cl. 1, 2
Bn. 1, 2
Hn. 1, 2
Hn. 3, 4
Tpt. 1, 2
(8va)
Vn. 1
Vn. 2
[arco]
Va.
p
Clar.
selt- sam A- ben- theu- er, welch' tol- les
Laura
wär' mir ein net- ter An- ver- lob- ter, ei, ein net- ter An- ver-
Gom.
Kalbs- ge- sicht! Du fre- cher Wicht!
Gast.
Kalbs- ge- sicht! Du Kalbs- ge- sicht!
Ambr.
drü- cken! Die- ser Spaß ist zum Ent- zü- cken, doch ist's Zeit, sich bald zu
Pant.
satt die tol- len Pos- sen, längst schon hat es mich ver- dros- sen, nun hab'
A
Kalbs- ge- sicht! Seht das Kalbs- ge- sicht!
T
Kalbs- ge- sicht! Seht das Kalbs- ge- sicht!
Vc.
p
Cb.

495

137
Fl. 1, 2
Ob. 1, 2
Cl. 1, 2
a 2
Bn. 1, 2
Hn. 1, 2
a 2
Hn. 3, 4
a 2
Tpt. 1, 2, 3
p
Vn. 1
(8va)
Vn. 2
Va.
Clar.
Spott, kaum kann ich's tra- gen!
Laura
schlank, da würd' ich sa- gen:
Gom.
-gen, Pin- to! Pin- to! Pin- to, fre- cher _ Wicht!
Gast.
nicht! Pin- to! Pin- to! Pin- to, Kalbs- ge- sicht!
Ambr.
wend', e- he sich die Sa- che wen- de, _ e- he _ sich die _ Sa- che _
Pant.
Pos- sen, dum- mer Pos- sen, hab' sie satt die _ tol- len _ Pos- sen, _ hab' _ sie _
S
Ei, den Ver-
A
Seht _ doch nur das _ Kalbs- ge- sicht! Pin- to! Pin- to! Pin- to!
T
Seht _ doch nur das _ Kalbs- ge- sicht! Pin- to! Pin- to! Pin- to!
B
Vc.
p
Cb.
arco
p

139
Fl. 1, 2
Ob. 1, 2
a 2
Cl. 1, 2
Bn. 1, 2
Hn. 1, 2
Hn. 3, 4
(8va)
Vn. 1
Vn. 2
Va.
Clar.
Ich er- lie- ge! Gro- ßer
Laura
"Schö- ner Jüng- ling, vie- len
Gom.
Fort, ist das er- hört, ein solch' Be- tra- gen? Fort, hin- aus, Du fre- cher
Gast.
Pin- to, theu- rer Pin- to, mei- nen Dank, das ver- ges- se ich Dir
Ambr.
wend'! Führ- wahr, ein Klu- ger denkt an's
Pant.
satt! Die tol- len Pos- sen, hab' sie
S
-stand will er ver- lie- ren, ei, wo mag er ihn nur spü- ren, den Ver-
A
Was will er ver- lie- ren? Ei, wo mag er ihn nur spü- ren, den Ver-
T
Was will er ver- lie- ren? Den Ver- stand? Den Ver-
B
Was? Jetzt ver- liert er den Ver-
Vc.
Cb.
pizz.

141
Fl. 1, 2
a 2
Ob. 1, 2
a 2
Cl. 1, 2
Bn. 1, 2
Hn. 1, 2
Hn. 3, 4
a 2
[a 2]
Tpt. 1, 2
a 2
(8va)
Vn. 1
Vn. 2
Va.
Clar.
Gott, ich er- lie- ge, gro- ßer
Laura
Dank, schö- ner Jüng- ling, vie- len
Gom.
Wicht! Ein solch' Be- tra- gen! Fort, hin- aus, Du fre- cher Wicht! Hin-
Gast.
nicht! O theu- rer Pin- to, mei- nen Dank, nein, Dir ver- geß' ich's
Ambr.
End', ein Klu- ger denkt an's
Pant.
satt! Ich hab' es satt!
S
-stand! Ei, nun gar ver- liert er den Ver-
A
-stand will er ver- lie- ren, nun ver- liert er den Ver-
T
-stand! Jetzt ver- liert er den Ver-
B
-stand! Jetzt ver- liert er den Ver-
Vc.
Cb.

143
Vorwärts!
Fl. 1, 2
Ob. 1, 2
Cl. 1, 2
Bn. 1, 2
Hn. 1, 2
Hn. 3, 4
Tpt. 1, 2
Trb. 3
Tb.
Vorwärts!
Vn. 1
Vn. 2
Va.
Clar.
Gott!
Laura
Dank!"
Gom.
-aus!
Gast.
nicht!
Ambr.
End'!
Pant.
Narr, fort, hin- aus denn!
S
-stand! Nur fort, hin- aus, Du tol- ler Narr, fort hin- aus, fort hin-aus, fort hin-
A
-stand! Fort, hin- aus, fort hin-aus, fort hin-
T
-stand! Fort, hin- aus, fort hin-aus, fort hin-
B
-stand! Hin- aus, Du tol- ler Narr, fort hin- aus, fort hin-aus, fort hin-
Vc.
Cb.

K
147
Fl. 1, 2
a 2
Ob. 1, 2
a 2
Cl. 1, 2
Bn. 1, 2
Hn. 1, 2
Hn. 3, 4
[3]
Vn. 1
Vn. 2
Va.
Pinto
Ich bin Pin- to, ja Pin- to, Don
S
-aus, fort hin-aus, fort hin- aus!
A
-aus, fort hin-aus, fort hin- aus!
T
-aus, fort hin-aus, fort hin- aus!
B
-aus, fort hin-aus, fort hin- aus!
Vc.
Cb.

151
Fl. 1, 2
Ob. 1, 2
a 2
Cl. 1, 2
Bn. 1, 2
Hn. 1, 2
Hn. 3, 4
Vn. 1
Vn. 2
Va.
Clar.
Nur fort hin-aus, nur fort hin-aus!
Laura
Nur fort hin-aus, nur fort hin-aus!
Gom.
Nur fort hin-aus, nur fort hin-aus!
Gast.
Nur fort hin-aus, nur fort hin-aus!
Ambr.
Nur fort hin-aus, nur fort hin-aus!
Pant.
Nur fort hin-aus, nur fort hin-aus!
[ossia]
Pinto
Pin- to de Fon-se- ca! Und su- che mei- ne Braut, ja, ich
S
Nur fort hin-aus, nur fort hin-aus!
A
Nur fort hin-aus, nur fort hin-aus!
T
Nur fort hin-aus, nur fort hin-aus!
B
Nur fort hin-aus, nur fort hin-aus!
Vc.
Cb.

502

159
Fl. 1, 2
Ob. 1, 2
Cl. 1, 2
Bn. 1, 2
Hn. 1, 2
Hn. 3, 4
Tpt. 1, 2
Trb. 3
Tb.
Timp.
Vn. 1
Vn. 2
Va.
Pinto
S
A
T
B
Vc.
Cb.
mf
cresc.
p
tr
f
divisi
(Er stürzt, ganz außer sich, auf Gaston zu)
(schreiend)
schuld, ja, die- ser ist an Al- lem schuld!
O Du Räu- ber, Dieb, Be- trü- ger, o Du
pp
Ei, was ficht den Töl- pel
Ei, was ficht den Töl- pel
Ei, was ficht den dum- men Töl- pel doch nur
Ei, was ficht den dum- men Töl- pel
Ei, was ficht den Töl- pel an!
Ei, was ficht den dum- men Töl- pel an!

162
Fl. 1, 2
Ob. 1, 2
Cl. 1, 2
Bn. 1, 2
Hn. 1, 2
Hn. 3, 4
Tpt. 1, 2
Trb. 3
Tb.
Timp.
Vn. 1
Vn. 2
Va.
Gast.
Pinto
S
A
T
B
Vc.
Cb.
p cresc.
ff
f
mf
(tr)
(Gaston stellt sich zornig losbrechend, den Degen in der Hand)
schnö- der We- ge-lag'-rer, Du Räu-ber, Be- trü-ger, Du schnö- der We- ge- lag'- rer, Du
an? A- ber Pin- to, klei- ner Pin- to! Sag', wo hast du dei- ne
an? A- ber Pin- to, klei- ner Pin- to! Sag', wo hast du dei- ne
an? A- ber Pin- to, klei- ner Pin- to! O sag', o sag', wo hast du dei- ne
A- ber Pin- to! Wo hast du dei- ne

165
Più mosso ♩ = ♩.
Fl. 1, 2
Ob. 1, 2
Cl. 1, 2
Bn. 1, 2
Hn. 1, 2
Hn. 3, 4
Tpt. 1, 2
Trb. 3
Tb.
Timp.
Cym.
a 2
[a 2]
mf
f
fff
Più mosso ♩ = ♩.
Vn. 1
Vn. 2
Va.
Gast.
Pinto
S
A
T
B
Vc.
ff
Herr! Jetzt zieht Eu- ren De- gen! Die- se Schmach tilgt Eu- er
Dieb!
Braut?
Braut?
Braut?
Braut?

Gast.: Blut! Raus den De- gen, seid auf der Hut, sonst fallt Ihr so- fort mei- ner Wuth!

S: Herr!
A: Herr!
T: Herr!
B: Herr!

Jetzt zieht Eu-er'n De- gen! Die- sen Schimpf sühnt Eu- er Blut, fließ' es

508

509

510

M
190
(8va)
Fl. 1, 2
Ob. 1, 2
Cl. 1, 2
Bn. 1, 2
Hn. 1, 2
Hn. 3, 4
Tpt. 1, 2
Trb. 1, 2
Trb. 3
Tb.
Vn. 1
Vn. 2
Va.
[arco]
Clar.
Laura
jetzt braucht er sei- nen Mut!
Gom.
Gast.
jetzt fließt Blut!
Ambr.
jetzt fließt Blut!
Pant.
jetzt fließt Blut!
Pinto
(ängstlich)
Ich den
S
jetzt braucht Ihr Eu- er'n Mut!
A
jetzt braucht Eu- ren Mut!
T
jetzt fließt Blut!
B
braucht nur Eu- ren Mut, jetzt fließt Eu- er Blut!
Vc.
Cb.

512

199
N
Fl. 1, 2
Ob. 1, 2
Cl. 1, 2
Bn. 1, 2
Hn. 1, 2
Hn. 3, 4
Tpt. 1, 2
Trb. 1, 2
Trb. 3
Tb.
Vn. 1
Vn. 2
Va.
Gast.
S
A
T
B
Vc.
Cb.
a 2
ff
f
[arco]
pizz.
De- gen, die- sen Schimpf sühnt Eu- er Blut!
Herr, ziehet nun Eu- ren De- gen; die- sen

514

209
O
Fl. 1, 2
Ob. 1, 2
Cl. 1, 2
Bn. 1, 2
Hn. 1, 2
Hn. 3, 4
Tpt. 1, 2
Vn. 1
Vn. 2
Va.
Clar.
Gast.
Vc.
Cb.
p espress.
divisi
sein! Seht den Ar- - men, wie er bebt!
Zieht den

516

225
P poco meno mosso
Fl. 1, 2
mf
poco meno mosso
Vn. 1
divisi
pizz.
Vn. 2
(zu Gaston)
Pinto
Steckt den De- gen ein, Herr Rit- ter, steckt doch Eu- ren De- gen
Vc.
Cb.
229
Fl. 1, 2
Ob. 1, 2
mf
Bn. 1, 2
mf
divisi
pizz.
Vn. 1
Vn. 2
divisi
pizz.
Va.
mf
Pinto
ein, gu- ter Rit- ter, gu- ter Rit- ter, gu- ter Rit- ter, thut mir
Vc.
Cb.

518

237
Q
Fl. 1, 2
Ob. 1, 2
Cl. 1, 2
Bn. 1, 2
Hn. 1, 2
Hn. 3, 4
Tpt. 1, 2
Trb. 1, 2
Trb. 3
Tb.
Timp.
Vn. 1
Vn. 2
Va.
Laura
Gom.
Gast.
Ambr.
Pant.
S
A
T
B
Vc.
Cb.
mf
cresc.
f
ff
p
a 2
(tr)
Fort, hin- aus, Du fei- ger Wicht!
[beide]
Fort, hin- aus, Du fei- ger Wicht!
[beide]
Fort, hin- aus, fei- ger Wicht!
fort aus dem Stau- be Dich ma- chen, Du Jammer- ge- stalt! Fort, hin-
fort aus dem Stau- be Dich ma- chen, Du Jam- mer- ge- stalt! Fort, hin-
bald aus dem Stau- be Dich ma- chen, Du Jam- mer- ge- stalt! Fort, hin-
bald aus dem Stau- be Dich ma- chen, Du Jam- mer- ge- stalt! Fort, hin-

520

246
Fl. 1, 2
Ob. 1, 2
Cl. 1, 2
a 2
mf
cresc.
Bn. 1, 2
a 2
mf
cresc.
Hn. 1, 2
2
p
1
mf
Hn. 3, 4
3
p
cresc.
Trb. 1, 2
Timp.
tr
pp
cresc.
Vn. 1
Springbogen
pp
cresc.
Vn. 2
Springbogen
pp
cresc.
Va.
Springbogen
pp
[cresc.]
Pinto
(jämmerlich)
Ach, ich will ja ger- ne geh'n, nie sollt Ihr mich wie- der
S
seh'n!
A
seh'n!
T
seh'n!
B
seh'n!
Vc.
Cb.
pp
[cresc.

250
R
Fl. 1, 2
Ob. 1, 2
Cl. 1, 2
a 2
Bn. 1, 2
Hn. 1, 2
Hn. 3, 4
Tpt. 1, 2
[a 2]
Trb. 1, 2
Trb. 3
Tb.
Timp.
(tr)
Vn. 1
Vn. 2
Va.
Laura
Fort, hin- aus, Du fei- ger Wicht!
[beide]
Gom.
Gast.
Fort, hin- aus, Du fei- ger Wicht!
[beide]
Ambr.
Pant.
Fort, hin- aus, fei- ger Wicht!
Pinto
seh'n!
S
Fort, hin- aus, Du fei- ger Wicht und nie- mals laß Dich wie- der
A
Fort, hin- aus, Du fei- ger Wicht und nie- mals laß Dich wie- der
T
Fort, hin- aus, Du fei- ger Wicht und nie- mals laß Dich wie- der
B
Fort, hin- aus, fei- ger Wicht nie- mals laß Dich wie- der
Vc.
Cb.

254
poco a poco string.
a 2
Fl. 1, 2
Ob. 1, 2
Cl. 1, 2
Bn. 1, 2
Hn. 1, 2
Hn. 3, 4
Tpt. 1, 2
Trb. 1, 2
Trb. 3
Tb.
Timp.
poco a poco string.
Vn. 1
Vn. 2
Va.
Clar.
Ja,
Laura
Ge- - he! Geh'! Die- ses ist
Gom.
Gast.
[beide]
Ge- - he! Geh'! Die- ses ist
Ambr.
Pant.
Ge- - he! Geh'! Die- ses ist
S
seh'n! Die- ses ist der
A
seh'n! Die- ses ist der
T
seh'n! Die- ses ist der
B
seh'n! Die- ses ist der
Vc.
Cb.
pizz.
arco
cresc.
[cresc.]

258
S
Fl. 1, 2
Ob. 1, 2
Cl. 1, 2
Bn. 1, 2
Hn. 1, 2
Hn. 3, 4
a 2
Tpt. 1, 2
Trb. 1, 2
Trb. 3
Tb.
a 2
Timp.
(tr)
Vn. 1
Vn. 2
Va.
Clar.
Laura
[beide]
der Eh- - re Haus!
Gom.
Gast.
[beide]
der Eh- - re Haus!
Ambr.
Pant.
der Eh- - re Haus!
S
Eh- re Haus! Fort mit
A
Eh- re Haus! Fort mit
T
Eh- re Haus! Fort mit
B
Eh- re Haus! Fort mit
Vc.
Cb.
ff

262
Fl. 1, 2
Ob. 1, 2
Cl. 1, 2
Bn. 1, 2
Hn. 1, 2
Hn. 3, 4
Tpt. 1, 2
Trb. 1, 2
Trb. 3 Tb.
Vn. 1
ff
Vn. 2
ff
Va.
ff
Clar. Laura
[beide]
Nur fort, hin- aus! Die- ses
Gom. Gast.
[beide]
Nur fort, hin- aus! Die- ses
Ambr. Pant.
[beide]
Nur fort, hin- aus! Die- ses
(Der Chor umdrängt Don Pinto und zwingt ihn zum Rückgang)
S
Pin- to, fort mit Pin- to!
A
Pin- to, fort mit Pin- to!
T
Pin- to, fort mit Pin- to!
B
Pin- to, fort mit Pin- to!
Vc. Cb.

266
Fl. 1, 2
Ob. 1, 2
Cl. 1, 2
Bn. 1, 2
Hn. 1, 2
Hn. 3, 4
Tpt. 1, 2
Trb. 1, 2
Trb. 3
Tb.
Vn. 1
Vn. 2
Va.
Clar.
Laura
[beide]
ist der Eh- re Haus! Nur
Gom.
Gast.
ist der Eh- re Haus! [beide] Nur
Ambr.
Pant.
ist der Eh- re Haus! [beide] Nur
S
Fort mit Pin- to, fort mit Pin- to!
A
Fort mit Pin- to, fort mit Pin- to!
T
Fort mit Pin- to, fort mit Pin- to!
B
Fort mit Pin- to, fort mit Pin- to!
Vc.
Cb.

527

528

278
Fl. 1, 2
Ob. 1, 2
Cl. 1, 2
Bn. 1, 2
Hn. 1, 2
Hn. 3, 4
Tpt. 1, 2
Trb. 1, 2
Trb. 3
Tb.
Vn. 1
Vn. 2
Va.
Clar.
Laura
Gom.
Gast.
(Ambrosio hat sich Don Pinto immer mehr genähert; endlich wirft er ihn hinaus)
Ambr.
Pant.
S
A
T
B
Vc.
Cb.
ff
fff
10
[beide]
Fort, Don Pin- to!
Wicht, nur fort hin- aus, Du Kalbs- ge- sicht! Fort, Don Pin- to!

No. 21. Finale B

Heil sei Euch, Don Pantaleone, heil der Tochter, heil dem Sohne, den die

Lie- be Euch ge- schenkt! Preis der Weis- heit, Preis der Mil- de, die dem

533

22
Fl. 1, 2
pp
Ob. 1, 2
1
pp
Cl. 1, 2
mf leggiero
Bn. 1, 2
[1]
pp
Hn. 1, 2
Hn. 3, 4
pp
Vn. 1
Vn. 2
arco
pizz.
arco
Va.
arco
pizz.
arco
Gast.
(zu Ambrosio)
Nun, was sagst Du, Don Am- bro- sio?
Dacht't Du
Vc.
Cb.
pizz.
p

535

Nun, Herr Ritter, meinetwegen; da wir nichts gewinnen

konn- ten, scheint mir we- nig d'ran ge- le- gen, wer die Braut von dan- nen führ- te; wer die

Braut von dan- nen führ- te; da wir nichts ge- win- nen konn- ten, scheint mir we- nig d'ran ge-

*[The forte and fortissimo dynamics are to be used only when the cut occurs, in which case, Ambrosio does not sing.]

C
a 2
52
Fl. 1, 2
Ob. 1, 2
Cl. 1, 2
Bn. 1, 2
Hn. 1, 2
Hn. 3, 4
Tpt. 1, 2
Trgl.
Vn. 1
Vn. 2
Va.
S
A
Vc.
Cb.
arco
Möcht' es Je- der doch ge- lin- gen, den Ge- lieb- ten zu er- rin- gen durch der
Möcht' es Je- der doch ge- lin- gen, den Ge- lieb- ten zu er- rin- gen durch der
arco

Lie- be heil'- ge Mäch- te! Mög' sie mit des Va- ters

62
Fl. 1, 2
Ob. 1, 2
Cl. 1, 2
Bn. 1, 2
a 2
Hn. 1, 2
Hn. 3, 4
p
Tpt. 1, 2
1
(tr)
Trgl.
Vn. 1
Vn. 2
Va.
S
Se- gen al- lem Schick-sals- trotz ent- ge- gen ein zum Glück' der E- he
A
Se- gen al- lem Schick-sals- trotz ent- ge- gen ein zum Glück' der E- he
Vc.
Cb.

*Cfr. Clavier Ausgabe: Heil und Se-gen ed-les Paar! [tacet mm. 70–71].

544

545

E
84
Picc. 1, 2
Ob. 1, 2
Cl. 1, 2
a 2
Bn. 1, 2
Hn. 1, 2
Hn. 3, 4
Tpt. 1, 2
Tamb.
Cast.
Vn. 1
Vn. 2
Va.
pizz.
Clar.
Laura
Das wird ein Spaß, das wird ein Spaß!
Gom.
Gast.
Ei, ist er toll, ei, ist er toll?
Ambr.
-net- ten hör' ich klin- gen, dum trrrr um trrrr um trrrr um, Flöt' und
Pant.
Vc.

88
[a 2]
Picc. 1, 2 (Fl. 1, 2)
Fl. 1, 2
Ob. 1, 2
Cl. 1, 2
a 2
Bn. 1, 2
Hn. 1, 2
Hn. 3, 4
Tpt. 1, 2
a 2
Trgl.
Tamb. Cast.
a 2
Vn. 1
Vn. 2
Va.
Clar.
Wie sie la- chen, seht doch, seht doch!
Laura
Wie will ich da sprin- - gen, tan- - zen!
Gom.
Jetzt halt' ich, jetzt halt' ich Dich auf
Gast.
Di del du del du- i, di del du del du- i, när- risch,
Ambr.
Cla- ri- net- ten sin- gen, di del du del du- i, di del du del du- i, lu- stig,
Pant.
Ei, seht doch, ei, seht doch, 's ist zum
S
Di del du del,
Vc.

92
Fl. 1, 2
[a 2]
pp
Ob. 1, 2
[a 2]
pp
Cl. 1, 2
a 2
pp
Bn. 1, 2
pp
Hn. 1, 2
pp
Hn. 3, 4
p
Tpt. 1, 2
1
pp
Timp.
pp
[in G-D]
Trgl. Tamb. Cast.
Trgl.
Tamb. Cast.
pp
Vn. 1
arco
pp
Vn. 2
arco
pp
pizz.
f
Va.
arco
pp
pizz.
f
Clar.
Ich die Dei- ne! Ich die Dei- ne!
Laura
Tan- zen, tan- zen! Hei- sa! Hei- sa!
Gom.
e- wig! Dich auf e- wig! Dich auf
Gast.
när- risch! När- risch, När- risch! Di del di del
Ambr.
lu- stig! Lu- stig, lu- stig! Di del di del
Pant.
La- chen! 's ist zum La- chen! Di del di del
S
di del du del dum, dum, di del du del, di del du del dum, dum, di del di del
A
pp
Di del du del, di del dum, lu- stig sprin- gen, di del du del, di del dum, lu- stig
T
pp
Di del du del, di del du del dum, dum, di del du del, di del di del dum,
B
pp
Di del du del, di del du del dum, dum, di del du del, di del di del dum,
Vc. Cb.
arco pp
pizz. pp

96
F
Fl. 1, 2
Ob. 1, 2
Cl. 1, 2
Bn. 1, 2
Hn. 1, 2
Hn. 3, 4
Trgl. Tamb. Cast.
Vn. 1
Vn. 2
Va.
Laura
Gom.
Gast.
Ambr.
Pant.
S
A
T
B
Vc.
tr
3
pp
p
Tan- zen will ich, tan- zen, tan- zen! Ja!
e- wig, auf e- - wig!
di del di del dum, hei! Hei- sa! Hei- sa! Hei- sa! Hei!
di del di del di del di del dum, dum, dum, dum, dum!
di del di del di del di del dum, dum, dum, dum, dum!
di del di del di del di del di del di del di del di del di del di del di del di del di!
sprin- gen, lu- stig, hei- - di!
(Fistel)
dum, dum, hei- - di!
dum, dum, hei! Lu- stig, welch' ein Spaß!
pizz.
ff

100
Fl. 1, 2
Ob. 1, 2
Cl. 1, 2
Bn. 1, 2
Hn. 1, 2
Hn. 3, 4
Vn. 1
Vn. 2
Va.
Clar.
Laura
Gom.
Gast.
S
A
T
B
Vc.
Cb.
rit.
a 2
[arco]
pizz.
Se- lig- keit!
Und als- dann?
Sel'- ge
Sel'- ge

106
molto rit.
Fl. 1, 2
Ob. 1, 2
Cl. 1, 2
(tr)
morendo
Bn. 1, 2
Hn. 1, 2
Hn. 3, 4
pp
Tpt. 1, 2
ppp
Vn. 1
pizz.
molto rit.
Vn. 2
pizz.
Va.
pp
Clar.
Das dank' ich
Laura
Das dankt Ihr
Gom.
Das dank' ich
Gast.
Das dankt Ihr
Ambr.
Welch' ein
Pant.
O schön- ster
S
Lie- be!
A
Lie- be!
T
pp
Höch- ste Freu- de!
B
pp
Höch- ste Freu- de!
divisi
arco
pizz.
Vc.
pp
Cb.
pp

Tempo I
112
Fl. 1, 2
Ob. 1, 2
Cl. 1, 2
Bn. 1, 2
Hn. 1, 2
Hn. 3, 4
Tpt. 1, 2
Trb. 1, 2
Trb. 3 Tb.
Timp.
Trgl.
Vn. 1
Vn. 2
Va.
Clar. Laura
Gom. Gast.
Ambr. Pant.
S A
T B
Vc.
Cb.
a 2
ff
ppp
f
tr
divisi
arco
[arco]
f [beide]
nun Don Pin- to!
Spaß!
Tag!
Nun des Le- bens Freud' ent- ge- gen, je- der

Tag bring' neu- en Se- gen, vor- wärts auf des Glü- ckes Spur!

122
Fl. 1, 2
Ob. 1, 2
Cl. 1, 2
Bn. 1, 2
Hn. 1, 2
Hn. 3, 4
a 2
Tpt. 1, 2
a 2
Trb. 1, 2
Trb. 3
Tb.
Timp.
Trgl.
Vn. 1
Vn. 2
Va.
Clar.
Laura
[beide]
Sieh', uns win- ken sü- ße Won- nen, Zu- kunft steht voll lich- ter Son- nen, se- lig
Seht, Euch
Gom.
Gast.
[beide]
Sieh', uns win- ken sü- ße Won- nen, Zu- kunft steht voll lich- ter Son- nen, se- lig
Seht, Euch
Ambr.
Pant.
[beide]
Seht, Euch win- ken sü- ße Won- nen, Zu- kunft steht voll lich- ter Son- nen, se- lig
S
A
Seht, Euch win- ken sü- ße Won- nen, Zu- kunft steht voll lich- ter Son- nen, se- lig
T
B
Seht, Euch win- ken sü- ße Won- nen, Zu- kunft steht voll lich- ter Son- nen, se- lig
Vc.
[divisi]
Cb.

127
G
(tr)
Fl. 1, 2
Ob. 1, 2
Cl. 1, 2
Bn. 1, 2
Hn. 1, 2
Hn. 3, 4
Tpt. 1, 2
Trb. 1, 2
Trb. 3
Tb.
Timp.
Trgl.
Vn. 1
Vn. 2
Va.
Clar.
Laura
Gom.
Gast.
Ambr.
Pant.
S
A
T
B
Vc.
Cb.
a 2
p
mf
f
espress.
mf espress.
divisi
LAURA
[beide]
lacht die Ge- gen- wart! Se- - lig lacht die
lacht die Ge- gen- wart! Se- - lig lacht die
lacht die Ge- gen- wart!
lacht die Ge- gen- wart! Se- lig lacht die
lacht die Ge- gen- wart!

132
Fl. 1, 2
Ob. 1, 2
Cl. 1, 2
Bn. 1, 2
Hn. 1, 2
Hn. 3, 4
Tpt. 1, 2
Trb. 1, 2
Trb. 3
Tb.
Vn. 1
Vn. 2
Va.
Clar.
Laura
Gom.
Gast.
Ambr.
Pant.
S
A
T
B
Vc.
Cb.
a 2
p
cresc.
LAURA
[beide]
Ge- gen- wart! Ja, se- lig lacht die Ge- gen-
Ja, se- lig lacht die Ge- gen-
Ge- gen- wart!
Se- lig lacht die Ge- gen-
[divisi]

557

142
Fl. 1, 2
ff
Ob. 1, 2
ff
Cl. 1, 2
Bn. 1, 2
Hn. 1, 2
f
Hn. 3, 4
a 2
Tpt. 1, 2
Trb. 1, 2
Trb. 3
Tb.
Timp.
Vn. 1
Vn. 2
Va.
Vc.
Cb.

Ende der Oper

Critical Report

Sources

This edition of *Die drei Pintos* is based primarily on the full score that Mahler supervised for C. F. Kahnt.[1] The score was published as a lithograph of the copyists' manuscript and was included with rental material for this work. The total number of lithographs is unknown, but at least thirteen were prepared and none with Mahler's autograph insertions is known to survive. There has also been some correlation to the contemporary piano-vocal score.[2] While Mahler apparently knew of the piano-vocal score,[3] he probably did not supervise its preparation. Finally, the published libretto[4] has been drawn upon selectively for some readings of the underlay. For the ways in which the piano-vocal score and libretto have contributed to the edition, see the editorial methods and critical notes below.

Editorial Methods

As stated in the discussion of sources above, the primary source for this edition is the lithograph score issued by C. F. Kahnt in 1888, and it is to this that "the source" refers throughout the present section and the following section of critical notes. In certain isolated instances, however, readings from the secondary source, the piano-vocal score also issued by C. F. Kahnt, have been drawn upon to clarify oversights of the full score; all such instances have been reported in the critical notes. The extant performance parts have not been used for this edition because of the difficulties involved with ascertaining the appropriate markings and usage. As a study score, this edition relies on the authenticated source which the composer himself supervised.

Editorial additions to the source score are marked whenever they occur. Editorial slurs, ties, and hairpins are dashed. Editorial letter dynamics are set in bold (rather than the conventional bold-italic) typeface. Editorial articulations are placed in parentheses, as are added cautionary accidentals. Other editorial elements are placed in brackets.

The "Personen" list found on page 2 of the edition is transcribed from the source, which also includes the "Ort der Handlung" (provided in this edition only in the libretto). The list of instruments has been newly added for the edition. The titles of numbers follow the source. Numbers ending with thin-thin barlines and indications of the next number's meter signature have been changed to end with thin-thick barlines with the change of meter removed. Where break marks in the source are given on some but not all staves, the edition tacitly repeats them on all staves. Similarly, where fermatas are indicated for an entire system of the source, they have been regularized to appear above each bracketed grouping of the edition's score.

This edition retains the rehearsal letters found in the Kahnt score but also includes measure numbers for each of the twenty-two pieces (twenty-one numbers plus the "Entr'act") in *Die drei Pintos*. The order of instruments and voices in the Kahnt score follows modern usage and that has been maintained in the edition (with any regularizations or completions made as needed). Except where prevented by space considerations, the full scoring occurs at the beginning of each number in the edition, with a reduced score occurring on subsequent pages. Where expedient, instruments or voices share staves and are labelled appropriately. In the source, the violoncello and contrabass parts are often combined on a single staff when doubling the same part but usually occur on separate staves when they diverge; this practice is generally maintained in the edition. All instrument names and abbreviations are translated into English. The source makes a practice of repeating an instrument or voice name within the score whenever that instrument or voice enters; all such redundant indications have been removed for the edition.

In the source, tempo and other written directives meant to apply to the entire score are set at the top and often at the bottom of a system, and sometimes occur at one or two other places in between. This edition places the directives at the top of the system and above the violins if present (where violins are not present, the lower directive is placed above whatever comes next in the score order); where only a few instruments and voices are involved, the directive is placed only at the top of the system. Rehearsal letters are set at the top and bottom of systems in the source; the edition only places them at the top. The source consistently skips the letter "I" and this practice has been maintained.

Directives for the score have been regularized with respect to spelling and orthography. Most begin with a capital letter, except for terms traditionally set lowercase (such as *a tempo, rit., poco accel.*). Where appropriate, performance and stage directions in the source are set as footnotes in the edition. Abbreviations within such directions have been written out, punctuation has been added or adjusted for sense, and asterisks have been added within the score as needed to clarify the application of those directions. Parenthetical instructions found within the source score that are set as footnotes have had their parentheses removed. Expression marks and performance instructions for voices and instruments have been regularized with respect to placement, as have dynamic markings. The spelling and orthography of these marks and instructions have also been regularized, including, as applicable, their abbreviations. The instruction to divide string sections is usually *divisi* in the source and this term has replaced the few instances of *getheilt*. Dashing to indicate crescendos, etc. follows the source; gaps occurring within the dashing are filled in tacitly but more substantive gaps and omissions are reported in the critical notes. Positions of hairpins have sometimes been adjusted in relation to concurrent parts. Unnecessary periods that occur after many elements of the source, from letter dynamics to the titles of numbers, have been removed.

The cuts marked in the source and those added later (see "Mahler's Revisions for the Kahnt Score" below) are indicated in the edition; *segnos* have been included for those of the revision list so that they match those originating in the source. The source includes dialogue prompts before many of the numbers; for this edition all such cues have been removed from the score and are collected under "Text Cues in the Kahnt Score" below.

The original clefs of the source are retained in general with any substantive changes reported in the critical notes. However, where the source changes a clef (as from bass to tenor in the violoncello) or uses *all'ottava* notation simply because of a lack of space, the edition employs the usual clef or octave notation without comment. Also, the source assumes transposition down by one octave for tenor parts using treble clef, but this is made explicit in the edition through use of the transposing treble clef.

Redundant accidentals (including those on notes tied over barlines) have been tacitly removed. Cautionary accidentals of the source are retained where they clarify readings. In some instances this edition adds cautionary accidentals in parentheses to clarify potentially ambiguous passages. Double sharps have been cancelled with a single sharp in the edition (rather than with a natural and sharp as in the source). The source presents the horn, trumpet, and timpani parts without key signatures and with accidentals written in where Mahler deemed them necessary. This edition includes the appropriate key signatures for each of these parts such that all accidentals thereby rendered redundant have been removed. In the case of notes that are inflected by the added key signatures but that are meant to be uninflected (this being indicated by a lack of notated accidentals in the source), cancelling natural signs have been added in brackets. In the timpani part, tuning indications found in the source are retained but are here regularized to follow the model of "in D-A"; German-language pitch designations are printed in English (e.g., B becomes B♭). In the edition, such indications are generally placed immediately after the final note preceding any needed change; when this involves moving the indication from its original position in the source, the situation is reported in a critical note.

With paired woodwind and brass instruments which share a single staff, common stemming has been used in the edition where practical and when doing so improves clarity. Opposing stemming is always used when the notation involves different note values and rest patterns between the two instruments. The source includes voicing numerals to indicate when only one or the other paired instrument plays. However, it is more common to find upstems with rests underneath when only the first instrument is to play and downstems with rests above for the second. In the edition, voicing numerals are used more consistently than in the source to indicate that only the first or second instrument is playing in order to dispense with superfluous or redundant rests and allow for single-line stemming. Likewise, the source includes the marking *a 2* when both instruments play in unison, but it sometimes indicates this by using both up- and downstems on the notes. In this edition, the general practice is to use *a 2* in such situations and to avoid double stemming in unison passages. It should be understood that all voicing numerals and *a 2* indications that have been added have not been placed in brackets when they simply express what is already explicitly expressed in the source by another means. These markings (as well as "solo" indications and abbreviations such as "Tb." which replace the usual use of a voicing numeral) have also been repeated as necessary to avoid ambiguity, such as when an instrumental line continues over a page turn of the edition. In the few instances where two solo voices share a staff and sing in unison, the indication "beide" has been added in brackets.

Articulation marks have been regularized with respect to placement. In a pattern of clearly notated articulations, such as staccato dots, if one or two are not visible due to the crowding of other notational elements, those are tacitly provided. Articulations that are missing but seem called for by the context or by parallel passages have been added, as noted above, in parentheses. However, in cases where two parts of the chorus share a single staff, articulations in one part are tacitly applied to the other as well. Wedges in the source have been set as strokes instead. Where dots appear above a measured-tremolo note, those dots have been taken to signify staccato articulations rather than dots of division (since, in most cases, dots are not part of the notation to indicate division, the slash or slashes through the beam generally occurring alone). With regard to measured tremolo notation itself, tremolo of eighth and sixteenth notes has been written out, except in the case of the triangle, whose notation has been left alone unless noted in the critical notes. Beaming patterns have been adjusted to follow modern conventions. Groupette numerals have been regularized with respect to placement and, where appropriate, include horizontal brackets to enclose unbeamed notes and rests. Trills are set with or without ties as found in the source, except that any extra tie to the suffix notes has been removed.

The source is often unclear in its notation of slurs within systems and especially between systems. A slur indicated to be continued at the end of one system might not continue to the next, or a slur clearly marked to end at one system might be followed by a continuation at the beginning of the next. In this edition, an attempt has been made to treat slurs with accuracy and consistency, their notation being tacitly regularized in relation to concurrent parts or to parallel passages in the same or another part. Slurs are tacitly added to appoggiaturas where they are missing in the source. When a single note serves as both the end of one slur and the beginning of another, the two slurs are combined into one continuous slur, except where such treatment clearly disrupts the overarching phrasing indicated in the source. Slurs are also extended to enclose ties according to modern convention. Where necessary, slurs in vocal parts have been adjusted to maintain the general practice in the source of having one slur cover one syllable of text. The double slurs which connect common-stemmed chords in the source have been reduced to single slurs in the edition.

The text underlay of the edition is based primarily upon that of the source score. Kahnt published the score and the libretto separately, and conflating the two texts for the text underlay would have distorted needlessly the perfectly viable text underlay of the score. For the most part, the readings are rather close, and the divergences are slight and often reflect word choice rather than a wholly divergent meaning. Still, some readings of the libretto (reported in the critical notes) have been adopted in the underlay of the edition, and the libretto has also been drawn on tacitly for some punctuation and some capitalization of pronouns.

The underlay of the Kahnt score has been edited as follows: commas have been added for sense and to separate repeated words and phrases; missing apostrophes have been added; words that follow periods, exclamation points, and question marks have been capitalized where necessary; and words that follow commas and semicolons are placed in lowercase to follow prose capitalization style (poetic capitalization occurs in the edition of the libretto). All other instances in which the text underlay of the Kahnt score has been altered are reported in the critical notes.

Critical Notes

These notes describe readings of the source score where they differ from the edition in ways not described by the above editorial methods. Following are the abbreviations for the instruments and voices: Picc. = Piccolo; Fl. = Flute; Ob. = Oboe; Cl. = Clarinet; Bn. = Bassoon; Hn. = Horn; Tpt. = Trumpet; Trb. = Trombone; Tb. = Tuba; Timp. = Timpani; Cym. = Cymbals; B. Drum = Bass Drum; Trgl. = Triangle; Tamb. = Tambourine; Cast. = Castanets; Ruthe = Ruthe; Vn. = Violin; Va. = Viola; Clar. = Clarissa; Inez = Inez; Laura = Laura; Gom. = Gomez; Gast. = Gaston; Ambr. = Ambrosio; Pant. = Pantaleone; Pinto = Pinto; Wirth = Der Wirth; S = Soprano; A = Alto; T = Tenor; B = Bass; Vc. = Violoncello; Cb. = Contrabass. In reports of paired instruments sharing a single staff, the instruments are specified as, for instance, "Ob. 1," "Ob. 2," or "Ob. 1-2" according to how they are presented in this edition, even if the designations are editorial. Notes (including grace notes) are numbered consecutively within a measure; where it is necessary to count notes sounding simultaneously, these are numbered from bottom to top. Where appropriate, chords or beats are numbered rather than specific notes. Pitches are indicated using the system in which middle C = c'.

No. 1. Ensemble

Mm. 5–9, Vc. remains in bass clef throughout, but with *8va* indication from m. 5, note 2 to m. 8, note 1 and with *loco* indication at m. 8, note 2. M. 27, Vn. 2, notes 14–15 have slur. M. 47, chorus, underlay lacks punctuation (edition adopts exclamation point of libretto). M. 78, Timp. has "A-E" (tuning moved to m. 23 in edition). M. 81, equation reads "($\frac{3}{8}$ = ♩♩♩)". M. 84, Vc., note 4 lacks augmentation dot. M. 90, Vc., note 1 has staccato dot (rather than stroke). M. 99, Vn. 2, note 10 is a♯". M. 102, Hn. 4, notes 2–3, each lacks first ledger line below staff. M. 107, Bn. 1-2, note has augmentation dot. Mm. 124–25, Fl. 1 has interior slur from note in m. 124 to note 1 in m. 125. Mm. 141–42, Hn. 1-2 and Hn. 3-4, hairpins beginning in m. 141 are continued as a single series of dashes in Hn. 1-2 in m. 142. M. 147, second half of bar, score literal is *molto rit.*; removed since Mahler added same instruction in m. 148. Mm. 148–50, chorus, notes and underlay are lacking in source (added from piano-vocal score, p. 13). M. 162, original instruction for chorus (before Mahler's revision) reads "Die Studenten in feuriger Bewegung ab." M. 163, Ob. 1-2, note 7 lacks ledger line. M. 191, Va., chord has staccato dot.

No. 2. Rondo a la Polacca

Initial tempo marking is from piano-vocal score (p. 16), where it is spelled "Commodo." M. 4, Bn. 1, notes 3–4 are lacking. M. 7, Vn. 2, chords 1–2, each has staccato dot. M. 16, Bn. 1-2 has *p*. M. 22, Cl. 1, note 3 has staccato dot. Mm. 29–33, 48–51, 56–68, and 73–77, Tpt. 1-2 staves mistakenly labelled for Hn. 3-4. M. 45, Vc., notes 4–5 have slur. Mm. 51–52, Hn. 1-2 notated "in C" (with "in F" returning in m. 53). M. 57, Va., note 18 is b♯'. M. 61, Bn. 1, note 5 has both upstem and downstem with eighth rest below. M. 70, Cb., note 1 has *p*. M. 71, Cb., notes 2–3, each has staccato dot.

No. 3. Terzettino

M. 12, Wirth, note 1 has sforzando mark. Mm. 44–45, Cl. 1-2, chord of m. 44 is tied to chord 1 of m. 45.

No. 4. Romanze von dem verliebten Kater Mansor

Initial tempo marking (connoting mood rather than denoting tempo) is from piano-vocal score (p. 22). M. 1, Vn. 2, note 3 lacks notehead. Mm. 16 and 25, dialogue of source score refers to spoken lines of libretto; in a concert performance it may be possible to eliminate the dialogue entirely and sing the number without interruption.

No. 5. Seguidilla a dos

M. 25, Gast., notes 1–2, underlay has period (edition adopts exclamation point of libretto). Mm. 25–26, Va. lacks crescendo dashing. M. 47, Gast., notes 1–2, underlay has period (edition adopts exclamation point of libretto). M. 54, Bn. 1, note 2 lacks notehead. M. 86, Va., note 11 is f'. M. 89, Vc., note 6 has staccato dot.

No. 6. Terzett

Timp. has "H-Fis (tief)" for initial tuning. M. 1, Vn. 1, notes 4–5 are c×"–d#". Mm. 3–4, Gast. enters; entrance corrected to mm. 2–3 based on piano-vocal score (p. 31). M. 16, Gast. and Pinto, underlay has exclamation point. M. 17, Pinto, note 5 is eighth note. M. 18, Pinto, note 1, underlay has period (edition adopts exclamation point of libretto). M. 28, Gast., notes 1–2, underlay is "Gerade." M. 86, Va., note 3 lacks first ledger line above staff. M. 86, Gast., underlay has period (edition adopts exclamation point of libretto). M. 111, Ob. 1, trill lacks wavy line. M. 115, in the note (which appears as the footnote on page 103 of the edition), "unten" refers to the position of Pinto's staff on the bottom of the source's system of mm. 115–18. M. 123, Vc., note is downstemmed. M. 126, Ambr., *ossia* passage continues (matching main line). M. 127, Timp. has "in D-G (tief)" (tuning moved to m. 1 in edition). M. 140, Vc., notes 3–4 are b'–b'. M. 141, all cue notes are on staff in parentheses; Ob. 1, Cl. 1, and Bn. 1, cue note lacks staccato dot; Ob. 1, cue note lacks ♮; Vn. 1, cue note lacks slur; Vn. 2, cue notes not in source; Va., cue note lacks slur. M. 154, Gast., closing quotation marks in underlay are from libretto. M. 182, Cb., note 4 is c#'. Mm. 182–83, Cl. 1-2 lacks crescendo dashing. M. 183, Bn. 1-2, notes 8–9 are b#–c#'. M. 198, Ambr., note 4, underlay is "denn" (edition adopts "dann" of libretto). M. 206, Va. and Vc., beat 4 has *f*. M. 209, Vc., second part, note 4 has #, note 6 has ♮, note 7 has #. M. 212, Vn. 2, both parts, note 1 lacks augmentation dot. M. 223, Ambr., note 1 lacks augmentation dot. M. 253, Hn. 3-4, chord 1 has *mf*. Mm. 253–55, Ob. 1-2 has crescendo hairpin in mm. 253–54 (instead of *cresc.* with dashing as added in edition; dashing is added through m. 255). M. 255, Timp. has "H-Fis (tief)" (tuning moved to m. 130 in edition). M. 260, Bn. 1-2, notes 3–4 are eighth notes. M. 264, Pinto, note 3 lacks augmentation dot. Mm. 271–77, Vn. 1 and Vn. 2, the single crescendo dash in m. 271 has been continued into m. 277.

No. 7. Finale

M. 4, Ob.1, note 2 lacks fractional beam. M. 6, Timp. has "in D-A" (tuning moved to m. 1 in edition). M. 49, Pinto, note 4 lacks augmentation dot. M. 63, Gast., note 5 is d". M. 74, Pinto, extra quarter rest is after note 1. M. 78, Vn. 2, whole notes lack measured tremolo indication. M. 141, Timp. has "in Es-B" (tuning moved to m. 67 in edition). M. 159, Timp. has "in C-G" (tuning moved to m. 158 in edition). M. 161, Hn. 1-2, chord 1 has staccato dot. M. 167, Timp. has "D-B" (tuning moved to m. 165 in edition). M. 191, Fl. 1, note 2 lacks notehead. M. 201, Pinto, underlay is lowercased. M. 214, Timp. has "in D-A" (tuning not utilized in edition). M. 218, Vn. 2, hairpin extends only to end of measure (before page break of source). Mm. 221–24, Va. lacks diminuendo dashing. M. 224, Va., note 1 has *p* (moved to m. 225, note 1 in edition). M. 227, Ob. 2, note 2 is a'. M. 250, Cl. 1-2, chords 3 and 5, each has sforzando mark (rather than marcato accent). M. 254 has footnote ("Diese im Clavier-Auszug fehlende Stelle der Inez noch einzufügen.") referring to a misprint in the piano-vocal score (p. 65). M. 263, Hn. 1 has incorrect "tie" drawn betweeen notes 1 and 2. M. 264, Vc., notes occur before page break of source, without indication of division of cellos into two parts as of the next measure; in the edition, the notes of m. 264 are given only to the second part. M. 272, Vc., first part, note 2 is quarter note tied to eighth note. M. 278, Hn. 3-4 has change to bass clef (moved to m. 254 in edition); source lacks warning change to treble clef (added in m. 286 in edition). M. 282, Gast., note 6 is e". M. 289, T lacks *(wollen ihn aufmerken)* indication. M. 292, Cl. 1-2, note 1 lacks augmentation dot. M. 299, Bn. 2 has whole rest (not indicated to play the quarter-note d and without continuation of slur over break of source between m. 298 and m. 299). M. 322, T, note 3, underlay has exclamation point. Mm. 349–57, T and B are combined on single staff mistakenly headed by treble clef (notes are clearly meant for bass clef and are corroborated in piano-vocal score, pp. 72–73). M. 358, Vn. 2 and A, note 1 has ♮ (moved to note 2 in edition). Mm. 371–72, Vn. 1, continuation of hairpin in m. 372 is not preceded by beginning in m. 371 (over a system break of source).

Entr'act

M. 16, Vn. 2 has fermata on second quarter rest. M. 43, Bn. 1-2, chord is d + a. M. 58, Hn. 4, note lacks ♭; reading is from piano-vocal score which has c# (p. 75). Mm. 59 and 60, Ob. 1-2, note 7 has augmentation dot. M. 64, score lacks crescendo dashing. M. 106, Hn. 1, note has staccato dot. M. 108, Cl. 1, Hn. 1, and Va., note 4 has staccato dot. M. 113, Hn. 1, note 1 has *pp*. M. 117, Va., notes 4–7 are eighth notes. M. 171, Cl. 1-2, chord 1 has *f*. M. 173, Fl. 1-2 and Ob. 1-2, note 1 is eighth note.

No. 8. Introduction und Ensemble

Timp. has "in B. F. (tief)" for initial tuning. M. 3, Vn. 2, note 1 has sforzando mark. M. 26, Va., note 1 is e♭. M. 28, Hn. 2, note 4 is g'. M. 33, chorus, note 3, underlay is "doch" (edition adopts "nur" of libretto and as found in m. 30). M. 46, chorus, beats 3–4, underlay is "wicht'ge" (edition adopts "neue" of libretto). M. 58, Timp. has "in B-F" (tuning moved to m. 26 in edition). M. 67, Bn. 2, note is a. M. 68, Cl. 1, note 5 appears to be a'. M. 70, Va., note 1 is d. M. 107, Clar., note is a'. M. 110, Va., note 1 has staccato dot. M. 112, Ob. 2, note is two tied half notes. Mm. 114–18, Bn. 1-2 staff mistakenly labelled for Cl. M. 119, Laura, underlay has period (replaced with exclamation point). M. 123, Ob. 1, note has ♭. M. 124, Hn. 4, note 1 is double-dotted. M. 124, Clar., note 1 has ♮ (moved to note 2 in edition). M. 124, T, note 3 lacks augmentation dot. M. 128, Cl. 1-2, chord 2 lacks fractional beam. M. 138, Ob. 1-2 and Hn. 1-2, each has *p*. M. 139, Ob. 1-2, note 9 has staccato dot. M. 143, Cb., note 7 lacks ♭. M. 151, S, note lacks ledger line. M. 178, Pant., rest is eighth rest. M. 180, Fl. 1, Ob. 1, and Bn. 1, rests are 16th rests. M. 185, Pant., note 2 is eighth note. M. 186, Vn. 2, note 1 lacks trill and wavy line. M. 189, Fl. 1 and Picc., rests are 16th rests. M. 191, Va., notes 1 and 3, each lacks trill and wavy line. Mm. 192, 193, and 194, Vn. 2, note 3 lacks fractional beam. M. 202, Ob. 1-2 and Cl. 1-2, chord 1 has staccato dot. M. 203, Fl. 1-2, Ob. 1-2, and Cl. 1-2, rests are 16th rests. M. 203, chorus, parenthetical underlay lacks punctuation (exclamation point added). M. 205, Fl. 1, Ob. 1, and Cl. 1, rests are 16th rests. M. 217, Pant., note 1 is dotted quarter note, note 2 is eighth note. M. 217, Vc., cue-sized note in parentheses (in case of the cut) is neither present in source nor indicated by a performance note. M. 227, Hn. 1-2 has crescendo dashing. M. 231, Vn. 1, note 3 has staccato dot. M. 241, Bn. 1-2, beat 3, common-stemmed chord is beamed to downstemmed note. M. 241, Vc., note 9 is F♯. Mm. 257–58, A has slur from note in m. 257 to note 2 in m. 258. M. 280, Cl. 1, note 2 has ♮. M. 300, Laura, underlay lacks punctuation (exclamation point added). M. 302, Vn. 2, note 2 appears to be e♭″. M. 313, Cl. 1-2, chord 2 has *f*. M. 326, Vc., second note in measured tremolo is positioned higher than the first, but it lacks one ledger line. M. 336, Clar., note 1 has ♭ (moved to note 3 in edition). M. 339, Fl. 1, Ob. 1, Cl. 1-2, Bn. 1-2, each lacks cue-sized rest in parentheses (added in edition in line with performance note).

No. 9. Ariette

M. 3, Laura, verse 2, notes 1–3, underlay is "Höchste Lust" (edition adopts "Reinstes Glück" of libretto). Mm. 3–4, Laura, verses 1 and 2, quotation marks in underlay are from libretto. Mm. 9–10 and 18, Laura, verse 1, quotation marks in underlay are from libretto. Mm. 9–20, Laura, verse 2, underlay is missing in source (edition adopts text of libretto). M. 13, Fl. 1, note 4 has ♯ (moved to Fl. 2, note 4 in edition). M. 16, Vc., note has staccato dot.

No. 10. Rezitativ und Arie

Title in source is "No. 10. Arie." Initial tempo marking is from piano-vocal score (p. 106). M. 4, Clar., directive has "Recit"; "Recit." is also written at the top of the score. M. 12, Vn. 1, note 3 has ♭ (deleted with reference to piano-vocal score, p. 106). M. 79, Va. has quarter rest after note 2. M. 113, Vn. 1, rest is eighth rest. M. 113, Cb., note 1 lacks *f*. M. 131, Clar., notes 1–4, underlay is "mög" (edition adopts "mag" of piano-vocal score, p. 110). M. 137, Clar., note 3 lacks notehead. Mm. 155–56, Ob. 1, note of m. 155 and notes 1–2 of m. 156, each has staccato dot. M. 162, Vc., note 2 has *arco* indication (moved to m. 160, note 2 in edition).

No. 11. Duett

M. 4, Gom., note 8, underlay is "ich" (edition adopts "sie" of libretto). M. 7, Vn. 1, note 1 has staccato dot. M. 7, Clar., notes 5–6, underlay is "Blicken" (edition adopts "Blicke" of libretto). Mm. 16–18, Clar. staff mistakenly labelled for Gom. M. 21, Gom., note 9 is eighth note. M. 25, Gom., note 4, underlay lacks punctuation (edition adopts exclamation point of libretto). Mm. 25–28, Hn. 1-2 staff mistakenly labelled for Tpt. M. 36, Cl. 1, note 2 is g. M. 50, Gom., notes 1–5, underlay is "Blumen" (edition adopts "Blüten" of libretto and as found in m. 32). M. 51, Vn. 2, notes 1–2, each note is two tied half notes. M. 68, *rit.* only appears above Clarissa's staff (instruction is set as score directive in edition). M. 70, Vc., notes 2–4 are in treble clef using the old system of notation in which notes are written an octave higher than they are to sound. Mm. 70–75, Mahler's revision note concerning the dynamics has been incorporated into the score, including the request of a decrescendo from *pp* to *ppp* in mm. 74–75 of the flutes, oboes, and clarinets (which entailed removing their *mf* dynamics from m. 75); the original dynamics of the bassoons, brass instruments, and strings in the last two bars have nonetheless been retained, except that the final dynamic has been changed from *pp* to *ppp*, and the score directive "dim. al - - - *pp*" has likewise been changed to end with *ppp*. M. 72, Hn. 3-4, notes 1–2, each lacks downstem.

No. 12. Terzett-Finale

M. 23, Laura, note 4, underlay has period (edition adopts exclamation point of libretto). M. 42, Bn. 2, note has ♮ (moved to m. 41 in edition). M. 47, Gom., note 3 lacks augmentation dot. M. 49, Laura, note 1 is eighth note (followed by two 16th rests); note 5 is eighth note (followed by one 16th rest). M. 52, Clar., note has *Etwas breiter* indication (before Mahler's revised addition of *Etwas breit* as score directive in m. 53). M. 69, Hn. 1, notes 4 and 6, each lacks fractional beam. M. 70, Clar., note 2 is eighth note. M. 71, Hn. 1, note lacks augmentation dot. M. 72, Ob. 1-2, note lacks downstem. M. 73, Va., note 3 is eighth note. M. 77, Gom., note 4 is g′. M. 80, Cl. 1, notes 4–7 are c″–d″–e″–f″. M. 81, Gom., note 2 has augmentation dot. M. 92, Fl. 1-2 has interior slur on notes 2–3. M. 94, Fl. 1-2 and Ob. 1-2, note 1 has *a 2* (moved to m. 88 in edition). M. 94, Vn. 2, note 3 has *ff* (moved to note 1 in edition); note 8 is b♭′. M. 101, Va., note 7 is f. M. 105, Hn. 3-4, Tpt. 1-2, and Vn. 2, beat 1 has staccato dot. M. 106, Cb., note lacks augmentation dot.

No. 13. Lied mit Chor

M. 10, Cl. 1-2, chords 3–4 are g′ + g″ – g′ + g″. Mm. 18–24, Timp. staff mistakenly headed by treble clef. M. 27, Hn. 1-2 has "in F" (moved to m. 22 in edition). M. 33, Hn. 3-4 has "in F" (moved to m. 1 in edition). M. 33, Tpt. 1-2 has "in F" (moved to m. 22 in edition). M. 34, Vc. and Cb., note 1 has *sim.* indication. M. 40, Vc. and Cb. are combined on one staff with the *p* under note 2 of Cb.   M. 49, Cl. 1, note 1 has voicing indication of "1" (moved to m. 47 in edition).   M. 57, Hn. 3-4, note 1 has *f*. Mm. 61–68, Timp. staff mistakenly labelled for Trgl.   M. 72, Vn. 1 and Vn. 2, note 6 has ♮.   M. 74, Fl. 2, note 1 lacks notehead but ♯ is present.   M. 85, Timp. has "in C. G." (tuning moved to m. 79 in edition).   M. 86, Laura, rest is eighth rest.   M. 92, Fl. 1-2, Ob. 1-2, and Cl. 1-2, beat 1, common-stemmed chord is beamed to downstemmed note.   M. 93, Fl. 1-2 and Ob. 1-2, beat 1, common-stemmed chord is beamed to downstemmed note.   M. 93, Laura, notes 4–5 are 32nd notes.   M. 96, Fl. 1-2 and Hn. 1-2, chord 3 has staccato dot (moved to chord 4 in edition).   Mm. 97–100 and 108, Timp. rolls notated with three slashes through note stems (rather than with trill signs and wavy lines).

No. 14. Duett

Timp. has "in D-G" for initial tuning.   M. 6, Ob. 1-2 and Cl. 1-2, note 1 has *a 2* (moved to m. 1 in edition). M. 9, Bn. 1-2, note 5 is f♯'.   M. 20, Va., note has ♭.   Mm. 74–75, Vc., notes 5–8 of m. 74 and notes 1–4 of m. 75 are in treble clef using the old system of notation in which notes are written an octave higher than they are to sound; treble clef also precedes concurrent notes of Cb. but is clearly not meant for them since Cb. doubles Bn. M. 80, Vn. 2, note 6 has ♯ (moved to note 4 in edition). Mm. 81–83, Ambr., notes and underlay are lacking in source (added from piano-vocal score, p. 135).   M. 101, source indicates entrance of two piccolos but lacks explicit confirmation of return of flutes for the rest of the number (return of flutes is given in m. 127 in edition). M. 108, Ob. 1 and Ob. 2, note 1 lacks ♯.   M. 116, Gast., note 2 is eighth note.   M. 128, Vc. has *pizz.* indication. M. 159, Cl. 2, note 3 is a' (deleted with reference to piano-vocal score, p. 139).   M. 160, Vn. 1, note 5 has staccato dot (moved to note 6 in edition).

No. 15. Terzettino

The footnote in the edition (see p. 398) is written above the initial tempo marking in the source. Source lacks explicit indication that only Bn. 1 is to play.   Mm. 16 and 38, Gast., quotation marks in underlay are from libretto.   Mm. 33 and 40, Laura, quotation marks in underlay are from libretto.

No. 16. Ariette

M. 4, Fl. 1-2 and Ob. 1-2, note 1 lacks augmentation dot.   M. 4, Cym. has quarter note, quarter rest, half rest, and *Becken ohn Cassa* (all moved to m. 3 in edition). Mm. 7–8, Vn. 1, Vn. 2, and Va., triple-stop chords, each is on single stem.   M. 21, *Gemächlich* only appears above Ambrosio's staff (instruction is set as score directive in edition).   Mm. 21 and 23, Vn. 1, all rests are 16th rests. M. 24, Ambr., note 5 has *string.* indication (before page break of source with same instruction set as score directive in m. 25).   M. 28, Bn. 1-2, chord 1 has staccato dot. M. 30, Ambr., note 6 is eighth note.   M. 34, Ambr., note 1, verse 3, underlay is "Man!"   M. 34, Ambr., note 4 is 16th note; note 6 is eighth note.   M. 35, Ambr., note 4 is quarter note.   Mm. 35–36, Vc., notes 2–8 of m. 35 and notes 1–2 of m. 36 are in bass clef (placed in treble clef in edition to match mm. 31–32).   M. 38, Timp. has whole rest after page break of source (eighth-note d and rests to fill out bar have been added).   M. 44, Va., note lacks augmentation dot.

No. 17. Rondo-Terzett

M. 8, Gom., note 3 is dotted eighth note, note 4 is 16th note.   M. 16, Vc., note 2 has augmentation dot. M. 21, Va., note 3 lacks augmentation dot.   M. 24, Vn. 1, note 2 is eighth note.   M. 25, Hn. 1-2, Vc., and Cb., note is quarter note tied to eighth note; Gom., note 4 is quarter note tied to eighth note.   M. 29, Gast., note 1, underlay has exclamation point (edition adopts question mark of libretto).   M. 41, Vc., chords 2–3, each has staccato dot.   M. 45, Fl. 1-2, last eighth note (d") is upstemmed with eighth rest below.   M. 55, Cb., chord 3 has staccato dot (moved to m. 56, chord 1 in edition). M. 58, Timp. has "D-G" (tuning moved to beginning of number in edition).   M. 59, Cb., note 2 appears to be f' (partially covered by slur).   M. 63, source has thinthick barline.   M. 67, Va., note 3 is B.   M. 68, Gom., note 4, underlay appears to be "ein" (edition adopts "in" of libretto).   M. 76, Gom., underlay has period (edition adopts exclamation point of libretto).   M. 77, Bn. 1-2 has *p*.   M. 79, Vn. 1, note 1 is double-dotted. M. 106, Timp. has "C-G" (tuning moved to m. 59 in edition).   M. 107, Vn. 1 has extra *p* written in staff.   M. 109, Cl. 1, note 3 lacks first ledger line above staff.   M. 112, Fl. 1-2 has *p*.   M. 116, Gast., note 1 has augmentation dot.   M. 131, Gom., notes 1–3, underlay has exclamation point.

No. 18. Chor

Timp. has "D-G" for initial tuning (and also in m. 40).   M. 7, S, note 2, underlay has exclamation point (edition adopts question mark of libretto).   M. 9, B lacks *(Einige)* indication.   M. 10, A lacks *(Einige)* indication.   Mm. 11–12, chorus, *(And're)* indications are from piano-vocal score (p. 160).   M. 16, chorus, *(Alle)* indications are from piano-vocal score (p. 160).   M. 26, chorus, note 1, underlay has period (edition adopts question mark of libretto).   Mm. 56–58 and 65, Tpt. 1-3, source has no specific indication that Tpt. 3 continues to play, but edition gives top notes to Tpt. 1-2 and bottom notes to Tpt. 3.   M. 58, chorus, note 1, underlay has period (edition adopts exclamation point of libretto).

No. 19. Mädchenlied

M. 2, Fl. 1-2 staff in source lacks voicing indication. M. 11, Vn. 1, note 2 has staccato dot.   M. 21, Bn. 1-2, note is single-stemmed.   M. 24, Solo Vc., note 3 has staccato dot.   M. 30, Bn. 1, note has staccato dot.   M. 35, chorus, note 4, end of underlay is unclear.   M. 39, chorus, note 4, underlay is "-de."   M. 44, Bn. 2, note lacks augmentation dot.   M. 50, Vn. 1, notes 4–6 are b♭"–a"–g".   M. 51, Picc., note 1 has *morendo* indication.

No. 20. Finale A

Timp. has "D-G" for initial tuning.   M. 6, Vn. 1, note 5 is e‴.   M. 7, resting Tpt. 1-2 staff has *f* (moved to m. 9 in edition).   M. 30, T and B, each lacks (*flüsternd*) indication.   M. 32, notes 2–4 and m. 33, note 1, Clar. and Laura, underlay is lacking in source (added from piano-vocal score, p. 171).   M. 37, Tb., note 2 is G$_1$.   M. 38, B, note 2, underlay has exclamation point (edition adopts question mark of libretto).   M. 57, Vc., notes are in treble clef using the old system of notation in which notes are written an octave higher than they are to sound.   M. 65, Solo Vc., notes are in treble clef using the old system of notation in which notes are written an octave higher than they are to sound.   M. 68, Timp. has "D-H" (tuning moved to m. 51 in edition).   M. 70, Bn. 1, note 3 is e′. Mm. 72–76, Vc., octave dyads are in treble clef using the old system of notation in which notes are written an octave higher than they are to sound.   Mm. 72–80, Timp., notes are tied.   Mm. 72–73 and 78–80, Cym., notes are tied.   M. 79, Ambr., *ossia* notes are added from piano-vocal score (p. 179).   M. 81, Vc., note 3 has *arco* indication (moved to note 1 in edition).   M. 93, Pinto, note 2 has *f* (moved to note 1 in edition).   M. 100, Hn. 2, note 1 has ♯ (moved to note 2 in edition).   M. 102, Hn. 1, note 1 has ♯ (moved to note 2 in edition).   M. 106 (and just into m. 107), Hn. 1-2 has crescendo dashing.   M. 107, Vc., note 5 has staccato dot.   M. 111, Ob. 1, note 3 is d♯″.   Mm. 111–13, Vn. 1 lacks crescendo dashing in mm. 111–12 and has *cresc.* indication on note 1 in m. 113. Mm. 112–13, Vn. 2 lacks crescendo dashing in m. 112 and has *cresc.* indica-tion on note 1 in m. 113.   M. 112, Vc., note 1 lacks crescendo dashing.   Mm. 112–13 and 113–14, Va. lacks crescendo dashing.   M. 128, A, T, and B, each lacks (*kichernd*) indication.   M. 129, Ob. 1-2, Cl. 1-2, and Bn. 1-2, beat 1 has *pp*.   M. 129, Pant. has whole rest after page break of source (quarter-note d with rests to fill out bar and underlay "-mehr!" have been added). M. 132, chorus, note 6, underlay has exclamation point (edition adopts question mark of libretto).   M. 136, chorus, underlay lacks punctuation (exclamation point added).   Mm. 139 and 143, Laura, quotation marks in underlay are from libretto.   M. 149, Vc. and Cb., rest is 16th rest.   M. 155, A lacks (*leise nachäffend*) indication. M. 156, T lacks (*leise nachäffend*) indication.   M. 157, B lacks (*leise nachäffend*) indication.   M. 158, Timp. has "in D-G" (tuning moved to m. 80 in edition).   M. 161, Tpt. 1-2 lacks crescendo dashing.   Mm. 161–62, Vn. 1 lacks crescendo dashing.   Mm. 162–63, Cl. 1-2 lacks crescendo dashing.   Mm. 162–64, Timp. lacks crescendo dashing. M. 165, equation reads "♩. = ♩".   M. 179, Bn. 1-2, chord 2 lacks augmentation dots.   M. 181, S, note lacks augmentation dot.   Mm. 183–85, Ob. 1-2 and Cl. 1-2, each lacks crescendo dashing.   M. 184, Va., chords 2 and 3, each lacks flag.   M. 201, Vc. and Cb., note 2 has *arco* indication (moved to m. 189 in edition).   M. 204, Va., chord 2 is f′ + a′.   Mm. 235–38, Cb. lacks *cresc.* indication and crescendo dashing.   M. 238, Bn. 1-2, Vn. 2, Va., and Vc., each lacks crescendo dashing.   M. 239, Hn. 3-4, chords 2–4, each has staccato dot (rather than stroke).   M. 242, Cl. 1-2, chord 2 has staccato dot.   M. 242, Cl. 2, note 2 has ♮.   M. 242, Hn. 1-2, chords 2–4, each has staccato dot (rather than stroke).   Mm. 247–48, Vn. 1, Vn. 2, and Va., each lacks crescendo dashing.   Mm. 249–50, Timp. lacks crescendo dashing.   M. 251, Trb. 3 and Tb., chord lacks augmentation dots.   M. 255, Laura, note 2 lacks augmentation dot.   M. 268, Va., chords 1 and 2, each lacks the two ledger lines.   M. 270, Hn. 1-2 and Hn. 3-4, chord 1 has ♭ signs (moved to chord 2 in edition).   Mm. 271 and 272, Pant., note 2 lacks sforzando mark.

No. 21. Finale B

Timp. has "D-G" for initial tuning.   M. 25, Ob. 2, note 1 has *pp*.   M. 33, Ob. 1, note 4 lacks first ledger line above staff.   M. 59, Vn. 2, note 7 lacks ledger line.   M. 66, Vn. 2, tremolo half note has only one slash.   M. 67, Vn. 2, notes 6–7 are a′–g′.   Mm. 67–69, Gast., note refers to the alternative passage but does not supply it (as has been done in the edition).   M. 71, Timp. has "C-G" (tuning moved to m. 20 in edition).   M. 71, Vc., half notes with measured tremolo indication have *fp*; Cb., half note with measured tremolo indication has *fp*.   M. 91, Cl. 1, note 1 is f♯″; Cl. 2, note 1 is d″.   M. 97, B, note 1 is d′ (with ♮ written at level of f′).   M. 99, Laura, underlay lacks punctuation (exclamation point added).   M. 111, Gast., notes 1–2, underlay (sharing staff with Gom.) is "dank' ich" (edition adopts "dankt Ihr" of libretto). Mm. 114–16, Trgl., each note has three slashes.   M. 126, Vc., note 8 lacks ledger line.   M. 139, Laura, Gast., and Ambr., note 1 lacks sforzando mark; A and B, note 2 lacks sforzando mark.   M. 140, Laura, Gast., Ambr., A, and B, notes 1 and 3, each lacks sforzando mark.   M. 141, Va., note 3 has staccato dot.   Mm. 143 and 144, Vc., note 4 has staccato dot.

Mahler's Revisions for the Kahnt Score

Presented here is the list of revisions that Mahler had planned for *Die drei Pintos*, and which he most likely made in August 1888, when he conducted the opera in Prague.[5] This list, which is among the materials at the Internationale Gustav Mahler Gesellschaft,[6] corresponds to the list that he discussed with Natalie Bauer-Lechner in October 1901, and which he intended to place as an appendix in the full score.[7] All the revisions that Mahler specified in the 1888 list have been implemented in the present edition. The following is based on Mahler's list. The original list referred to page numbers and system numbers in the Kahnt score; these have been replaced by references to specific measure numbers in the present edition. Material placed in brackets has been added but material in parentheses is from the original.

No. 1. Ensemble

Mm. 5–11, Trombone 3 tacet [Trombone 3 had doubled the Bass from the second beat of m. 5 to the first beat of m. 11].   M. 32, add "Etwas ruhiger" [at rehearsal letter B].   M. 90, add "Tempo I."   M. 100, add "Ruhig" [at rehearsal letter F].   M. 104, add "nachgeben!"

M. 148, add "molto rit." M. 150, add "(für den Regisseur) Sie schreiten in halben Takten um Gaston herum." M. 162, revise the stage direction to read: "Hinter die Studenten in feuriger Bewegung ab. Schnellschrit."

No. 4. Romanze von dem verliebten Kater Mansor

M. 50, [revise per Mahler's note]: letzter Takt *ff* statt *ppp*.

No. 5. Seguidilla a dos

M. 26, add "vi-" [at the first beat]. M. 28, add "-de" [at the end of the measure].

No. 6. Terzett

M. 180, score Bassoon 1 an octave higher [up to the first beat of m. 181]. M. 206, add "vi-" after the caesura // at the marking "Più mosso." M. 241, add "-de" at the fermata, just before the marking "a tempo."

No. 7. Finale

M. 29, delete the marking "string." M. 137, add "hervortretend" to the Cello. M. 225, add "hervortretend" to the Cello. Mm. 372–78, remove the Chorus (seven measures).

Entr'act

M. 2, Violins and Viola: change the dynamic from *pp* to *mf* at the marking "Alle pizzicati thematisch deutlich." M. 5, Clarinets: add: "Vorschläge sehr schnell auszuführen." M. 17, add "Sehr mässig." M. 19, Horn: add "verklingend." M. 21, Horn: add "verklingend." M. 28, add "rit." M. 29, change "Belebter" to "Più mosso." M. 37, add "Sehr Mässig" under "Tempo I" (rehearsal letter C). M. 43, add: "Bemerkung für den Dirigenten: Das *ppp* muss plötzlich und äußerst leise ausgeführt werden." M. 59, add "Sehr breit" ([at the meter change to] C). M. 65, add "wie früher" (at the 6/8 measure). M. 81, Clarinet 1 and Bassoon 1: add "sehr schnell." M. 97, add "im Anfang sehr mässig wie früher" ([at the meter change to] C under the marking "Allmählig etwas belebter"). M. 104, add "Nicht schnell" (at the 3/4 measure). M. 104, Horns, Viola, Cello: "sehr zart." M. 113, add "Sehr zart, a tempo moderato" ([at rehearsal letter] E). M. 137, add "Immer noch sehr zart." M. 145, add "Breit und schwungvoll (Von hier an erst im Tempo und dynamisch steigern)." M. 145, Strings: add "molto espr." M. 146, Strings: replace the staccato dots with sostenuto lines (under the first two eighth notes). M. 163, add "poco rit." M. 165, add "Wieder sehr breit" (at [rehearsal letter] J). M. 168, at the second half of the measure add "Più mosso." M. 174, add "molto rit."

No. 8. Introduction und Ensemble

M. 47, add "vi-" (at the end of the measure). M. 66, add (before the measure) "-de" and revise the measure [per Mahler's note]: Für den Fall des Sprungs erhält die erste Violins statt des f zwischen der ersten und zweiten Linie ¼ [ein Viertel, that is, quarter note] f in der Octave. Viol. II, Viola, Cello & Bass erhalten eine Viertelspause [quarter rest] zu. M. 103, add "Breit." M. 107, add "Tempo I" (at [rehearsal letter] D). M. 111, add "rit." M. 115, add "Breit." M. 119, add "Wieder vorwärts" (at [rehearsal letter] E). M. 126, add "Tempo I" (one measure before [rehearsal letter] F). M. 330, add "vi-" (one measure before [rehearsal letter] P) and revise measure [329 per Mahler's note]: Im Falle des Sprungs singen Clarissa u. Laura im 2. Takt [that is, the second measure of the Kahnt score's system, which is m. 329] statt "sterbe": "sterbe jede." M. 339, add "-de" and revise the measure [per Mahler's note]: Im Falle des Sprungs erhält Viol. I statt ⅛ [ein Achtel, that is, eighth note] f. Pause [a rest], Viol. II, Viola, Laura ¼ [quarter note] f wie Clarissa und die Silbe: "Lust."

No. 10. Rezitativ und Arie

M. 22, remove the alla breve marking ¢ (no change of meter signature). M. 38, add "Nicht Schleppen" (at rehearsal letter B). M. 64, add "rit. e morendo."

No. 11. Duett

Mm. 71–75, [revise the passage per Mahler's note regarding this system of his conducting score]: Im dritten Takt [m. 72] (bei rit.) erhalten Fl. Ob. u. Clar. statt des *ff: f* einen Takt weiter, dann [m. 74] statt des *ff* im vorletzten Takt *pp*, am Schluss [m. 75] *ppp*. Fag. Hörner im 2. Takt [m. 71] statt *ff: mf,* im übrigen wie Fl. Ob. Clar. Pos. statt *p: pp*.

No. 12. Terzett-Finale

M. 1, revise the tempo marking to read: "Drängend (nicht schnell)." M. 50, add "poco rit." M. 53, add the tempo marking: "Etwas breit." M. 66, add "Wieder etwas vorwärts gehen." M. 75, add "rit." M. 75, Gomez: over the phrase "Leb' wohl" add "Breit." M. 76, add "Nachgeben!" M. 82, add "Von hier an bis zum Schluss in steter Steigerung!" M. 94, add "rit." M. 96, add "Breit" (at [rehearsal letter] F). M. 99, add "Più mosso" [second half of the measure]. M. 100, add "accel." over the last quarter note. M. 105, add "rit."

No. 14. Duett

M. 1, add "vi-" [at the beginning of the measure]. M. 4, add "-de" [at the end of the measure].

No. 20. Finale A

M. 15, add "Maestoso" (at [rehearsal letter] A). M. 19, add "accel." M. 20, add "Allegro." M. 23, add "Maestoso." M. 30, add "Nicht eilen!" (at [rehearsal letter] B). M. 34, add "Etwas Zurückhaltend." M. 46, add "Vorwärts" (at [rehearsal letter] D). M. 51, add "Allegro moderato." M. 76, add "Etwas zurückhaltend." M. 84, add "rit." Mm. 108–10, remove the Chorus. M. 165, add a Beckenschlag at dynamic level *fff*.

No. 21. Finale B

M. 1, add "vi-" (at the very beginning of the measure). M. 47, add "-de" (at the end of the measure). M. 48, add "(Anfang der Nummer)." M. 48, [for the cut, revise orchestration per Mahler's note]: Ob. Clar. Fag. erhalten *ff*, Viol. I II *f*.

Text Cues in the Kahnt Score

The source contains cues to indicate the start of specific numbers in *Die drei Pintos* or to help coordinate the text and the music. The cues occur at the beginning of numbers and resemble those found in modern piano-vocal scores of musicals, where a certain spoken phrase after a character name indicates the beginning of the next musical number.[8] In the source the cues are minimal when compared to the actual spoken dialogue between numbers, and they probably functioned as an aide-mémoire for Mahler when he first performed the work.

The decision to use such short cues in the full score was probably a practical one. The amount of text between numbers is often greater than the dialogue found between the numbers in nineteenth-century editions of other German singspiels or operas, such as Mozart's *Die Zauberflöte*, Beethoven's *Fidelio*, or Weber's *Der Freischütz*, and the incorporation of spoken text with musical numbers would have been difficult in a copyist's score (it was much more customary to find fuller texts in a formally engraved score). Further, the fuller cues—along with complete stage directions and blocking diagrams—would have been part of a conventional prompt book. As complete as it is for the musical numbers, the full score that Mahler supervised did not contain all the other information associated with a performance. In addition, the piano reduction of the work lacks any such cues at the beginning of numbers. (Some dialogue cues occur within several numbers, but those are not of concern here.)

In this edition of *Die drei Pintos* the text cues have been removed from the full score and are presented below. Character names have been added in brackets where they are lacking and quotation marks have been added tacitly where needed. The source lacks cues for several numbers, as in the first number of each act, where the dialogue comes only later in the scenes that follow.

The text cues listed below provide a starting point for coordinating the spoken dialogue with the music. The cues should assist the conductor in making the appropriate entrances when the dialogue occurs. Nevertheless, the main source of the spoken text remains the libretto, and in some cases additional text or staging instructions are found in the libretto after the text cue or before the start of the relevant number. In concert performances, which may not necessarily include the complete dialogue of the opera, it would be useful to "set up" numbers by using more lines of dialogue than merely the cues found in the source. It is conceivable that a concert performance could also involve a narrator to provide a synopsis of the action between numbers.[9] Without a performing tradition on which to build, it seems best that modern productions combine faithfulness to Mahler's score with the ingenuity of the performers in bringing the opera to the stage.

No. 1. Ensemble

None (beginning of act 1; the text starts after the opening of the number).

No. 2. Rondo a la Polacca

[Gaston:] "bis auf den Letzten. Was aber dann?"

No. 3. Terzettino

[Gaston:] "Ambrosio, mein letzter Heller."
[Ambrosio:] "Ei! Ei!"

No. 4. Romanze von dem verliebten Kater Mansor

[Gaston:] "Fort Ambrosio!"
[Stage direction:] Inez sitzt abseits, bisher von Gaston und Ambrosio unbemerkt. Ambrosio nach den ersten Accorden: "Beim Himmel, Herr, da sitzt sie und hebt zu singen an!" Gaston: "Ein reizendes Wesen!"

No. 5. Seguidilla a dos

[Gaston:] "er kann wenigstens Alles werden."

No. 6. Terzett

[Gaston:] "Ich zeige, wie Ihr's zu machen habt. Ihr werdet mir's leicht absehen!" Pinto: "O, das ist herrlich!"

No. 7. Finale

[Pinto:] "Ein schönes Mädchen ist die beste Speise!" [Gaston:] "Bravo, Don Pinto, Ihr lernt schnell!"

Entr'act

None.

No. 8. Introduction und Ensemble

None (beginning of act 2; the text starts after the opening of the number).

No. 9. Ariette

[Laura:] "statt zu verzagen!" [Clarissa:] "Ach, Laura!"

No. 10. Rezitativ und Arie

[Laura:] "Muth! Wir finden einen Ausweg!" (Laura ab.)

No. 11. Duett

[Laura:] "taub und blind zu sein scheinen." (Laura ab.) [The libretto contains more dialogue before the sung text begins.]

No. 12. Terzett-Finale

None (segue from the previous number).

No. 13. Lied mit Chor

None (beginning of act 3; the text starts after the opening of the number).

No. 14. Duett

[Laura:] "auch ohne Ihre güt'ge Erlaubniss, Herr Grimbart!"

No. 15. Terzettino

None.

No. 16. Ariette

None.

No. 17. Rondo-Terzett

[Gomez:] "Jede Genugthuung!" [Gaston:] "Aber was verlangt Ihr!"

No. 18. Chor

[Gomez:] "Ich hoffe freudig, es wird gelingen!"

No. 19. Mädchenlied

[Clarissa:] "O Vater, unendlich glücklich!"

No. 20. Finale A

[Haushofmeister:] "Da ist er schon!"

No. 21. Finale B

[Pantaleone:] "als Eidam an Pintos Statt willkommen."

Notes

1. Carl Maria von Weber, *Die drei Pintos: Komische Oper in drei Aufzügen*, der dramatische Theil von Carl von Weber, der musikalische Theil von Gustav Mahler (Leipzig: C. F. Kahnt, [1888]), ed. no. 2953. See Rudolf Stephan, *Gustav Mahler: Werk und Interpretation* (Cologne: Arno Volk Verlag, 1979), 24 (item no. 2a). See also the reference to this score in the catalogue of Mahler's works prepared by Susan M. Filler, *Gustav and Alma Mahler: A Guide to Research*, Garland Composer Reference Manual, no. 28 (New York: Garland Publishing, Inc., 1989), xlvi–xlvii (item no. 53).

2. C. M. von Weber, *Die drei Pintos: Komische Oper in drei Aufzügen*, der dramatische Theil von C. von Weber, der musikalische von G. Mahler, Klavier-Auszug mit Text (Leipzig: C. F. Kahnt, [1888]), ed. no. 1455.

3. That Mahler must have been somewhat familiar with it is shown on page 123 of the lithograph score, where the indication "cfr. cl. Ausg." [consult the piano edition] occurs, referring to the piano-vocal score's simplified passage for Gaston in No. 21, mm. 67–69 (see page 543 of the present edition). Since Mahler is known to have supervised the full score and referred to it for his subsequent revisions, it is likely that he knew of this marking and, hence, of the piano-vocal score.

4. C. M. von Weber, *Die drei Pintos: Komische Oper in drei Aufzügen* (Leipzig: C. F. Kahnt, 1888).

5. Mahler conducted *Die drei Pintos* in Prague on 18, 21, 24, 29, and 31 August 1888.

6. Gustav Mahler, *Die drei Pintos* [notes for C. F. Kahnt] (Vienna, Archive of the Internationale Gustav Mahler Gesellschaft, Item no. N/Pintos/12a). This is the list of revisions previously presumed to be lost; see James Deaville, "The C. F. Kahnt Archive in Leipzig: A Preliminary Report," *Notes* 42 (March 1986): 511.

7. See the quotation from Bauer-Lechner's *Erinnerungen an Gustav Mahler* given above on page xvi of the introduction (cited by note 48). Mahler's manuscript of the opera and the other autograph materials related to the completed score had been part of the archives of C. F. Kahnt, Leipzig, but the materials have been subsequently lost. See the comments by Deaville, "The C. F. Kahnt Archive in Leipzig," 510–11, 513. The copyists' materials at the Kahnt archive have all been superseded by the completed score, which is the basis for this edition.

8. See Leonard Bernstein, *Candide* (New York: Amberson Enterprises, Inc., 1958). Text cues occur at the beginning of almost every number, starting with the first (p. 18). They are distinguished from the sung text by their placement (before the musical number), the size of type, which is smaller than the sung text, and brevity—none extends beyond a single typeset line.

9. For this purpose, the performer may wish to consult the synopsis provided by John Warrack in *Carl Maria von Weber*, 2nd ed. (Cambridge: Cambridge University Press, 1976), 262–63. The recording of the opera conducted by Gary Bertini (RCA: PRL3 9063, 1977 [LP]; 74321-32246-2 [CD, released 1995]) includes a plot summary by F. Willnauer with the liner notes.

Recent Researches in the Music of the Nineteenth and Early Twentieth Centuries
Rufus Hallmark, general editor

Vol.	Composer: *Title*
1–2	Jan Ladislav Dussek: *Selected Piano Works*
3–4	Johann Nepomuk Hummel: *Piano Concerto, Opus 113*
5	*One Hundred Years of Eichendorff Songs*
6	Etienne-Nicolas Méhul: *Symphony No. 1 in G Minor*
7–8	*Embellished Opera Arias*
9	*The Nineteenth-Century Piano Ballade: An Anthology*
10	*Famous Poets, Neglected Composers: Songs to Lyrics by Goethe, Heine, Mörike, and Others*
11	Charles-Marie Widor: *The Symphonies for Organ: Symphonie I*
12	Charles-Marie Widor: *The Symphonies for Organ: Symphonie II*
13	Charles-Marie Widor: *The Symphonies for Organ: Symphonie III*
14	Charles-Marie Widor: *The Symphonies for Organ: Symphonie IV*
15	Charles-Marie Widor: *The Symphonies for Organ: Symphonie V*
16	Charles-Marie Widor: *The Symphonies for Organ: Symphonie VI*
17	Charles-Marie Widor: *The Symphonies for Organ: Symphonie VII*
18	Charles-Marie Widor: *The Symphonies for Organ: Symphonie VIII*
19	Charles-Marie Widor: *The Symphonies for Organ: Symphonie gothique*
20	Charles-Marie Widor: *The Symphonies for Organ: Symphonie romane*
21	Archduke Rudolph of Austria: *Forty Variations on a Theme by Beethoven for Piano; Sonata in F Minor for Violin and Piano*
22	Fanny Hensel: *Songs for Pianoforte, 1836–1837*
23	*Anthology of Goethe Songs*
24	Walter Rabl: *Complete Instrumental Chamber Works*
25	Stefano Pavesi: *Dies irae concertato*
26	Franz Liszt: *St. Stanislaus: Scene 1, Two Polonaises, Scene 4*
27	George Frederick Pinto: *Three Sonatas for Pianoforte with Violin*
28	Felix Mendelssohn: *Concerto for Two Pianos and Orchestra in E Major (1823): Original Version of the First Movement*
29	Johann Nepomuk Hummel: *Mozart's* Haffner *and* Linz *Symphonies*
30–31	Gustav Mahler: *Die drei Pintos: Based on Sketches and Original Music of Carl Maria von Weber*